Preface

'Critical care' is a global term that covers a diverse set of services. Most people immediately think of the intensive care or therapy unit – the ICU or ITU. Intensive care is for very ill patients who can benefit from more detailed observation or treatment than can safely be provided on an ordinary ward. But critical care is also given in high dependency units (HDUs), which provide an intermediate level of care between ICUs and ordinary wards, and in specialist areas such as renal units or coronary care units. Critical care should be for patients with potentially recoverable conditions. It is high technology care, and the equipment and interventions in use are increasing in complexity all the time.

The Audit Commission chose this study because, while critical care is of vital, life-saving importance, services are fragmented, expensive and under pressure. And, while there is a strong database about the illnesses of patients, there has been a dearth of useful management information about critical care resources, the treatments given and their effectiveness. Mismanagement can have adverse effects on trust-wide performance and quality – for example, major surgery may be cancelled when critical care units are full. The report makes explicit the links between organisation, efficiency and quality. Key improvements will require the involvement of those at the highest level of the trust – a good test-bed of the new proposals on clinical governance. To help fill the information gap, the Audit Commission's study included a national survey of bed numbers and staffing resources in England and Wales that secured a 100 per cent response from trusts and 85 per cent response from general adult units.

The report is not a blueprint for the reconfiguration of the country's network of services. It does not consider the number of beds needed nationally, the workings of the National Intensive Care Bed Register, whether current patterns of transfer between hospitals are appropriate, or how to transfer patients safely. This is because the NHS Executive has just carried out regional reviews, based on the survey information reported here. Instead, the Audit Commission's recommendations are aimed at helping individual trusts to improve their services. During 1999, appointed auditors are working with each acute trust in England and Wales on a stock-take, and recommending how services for patients can be improved. The most detailed work has been restricted to general, adult critical care services. While most of the recommendations are directed at the doctors and nurses who run critical care units, this report will also be of interest to clinical directors of 'user' specialties, senior trust nurses, executive and non-executive board members, purchasers and policymakers.

Dr Richard Waite, David Bawden and Lucy McCulloch carried out the study, under the direction of Dr Jocelyn Cornwell and Dr Jonathan Boyce. Phillip Brough, Emma Cox, Louise Cloke, Dr Colin Ferguson, Tonia Ghista, Samantha Jackson, Jo Marsh, Dr Kathy Rowan, Dr Ian Seccombe, Mandy Sheppard and Paul Smith contributed directly as members of the study team or as consultants. Chris Balfe (as national audit co-ordinator) and other pilot auditors contributed to the development of the audit approach. Appendix 1 lists members of the advisory group, together with the NHS trusts visited. A wide range of people provided helpful comments on an earlier draft of the report. The Audit Commission is grateful to them all. As always, however, responsibility for the contents and conclusions rests solely with the Audit Commission.

Introduction

1. Two key characteristics make a value-for-money study of critical care timely:

- demand pressures lead to ever-increasing costs as more beds are funded, but demand still seems to outstrip supply; and
- many aspects of critical care services vary between trusts, partly due to the way in which services have developed.

Key pressures

2. Critical care units constitute a complex, diverse network of general and specialist services that interact with all areas of the hospital. The pressure on services could affect quality. Despite increasing bed numbers (described in Chapter 1), staff in most units:

- remember peak days when they had to refuse admission to patients needing care [**EXHIBIT 1A, overleaf**]; and
- sometimes discharge recovering patients earlier than they feel comfortable with, in order to make room for new, higher priority, admissions [**EXHIBIT 1B, overleaf**].

3. Such experiences result in calls for more resources, especially since these difficult decisions involve the most acutely ill patients in the hospital. But supply-side solutions – providing more critical care unit beds – are unlikely to work on their own. As has been found in other areas of the hospital, too few or too many beds both have adverse effects (Ref. 1). This report shows that supply can generate demand, resulting in further pressure, and suggests that better management of inappropriate demand and efficiency improvements are also required.

Diversity

4. Despite the use of a common label – 'the ICU' – units vary greatly in (Refs. 2, 3 and 4):

- *casemix:* the type of patients admitted to critical care units – how ill they are, what is wrong with them, whether their admission results from an emergency or is planned in advance;
- *quality:* survival rates, and the efforts put into improving the quality of life of survivors and the humanity with which relatives are treated when on the unit;
- *care management:* how long patients are kept in the unit, which interventions are provided and at what stage they are discharged from the unit; how the boundaries of what doctors do and nurses do are changing;
- *unit management:* who manages critical care units; how many doctors are involved, and how many specialise in the treatment of critically ill patients; how well staff communicate with each other; how well they are supported to cope with this very stressful working environment;

EXHIBIT 1A

Measures of the pressure on critical care beds

Some patients are refused admission because the unit is full*...

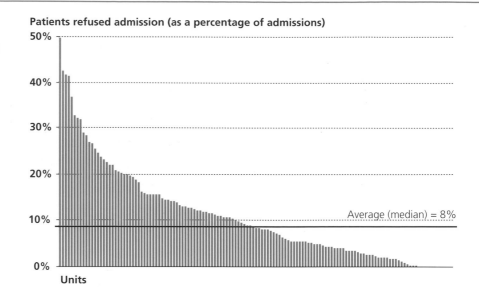

Patients refused admission (as a percentage of admissions)

Average (median) = 8%

Units

Source: Audit Commission survey 1997/98 (130 general ICUs, ICU/HDUs, ICU/CCUs and HDUs). More information on the main data sources is given in Appendix 2. The number of trusts or critical care units on which each of the report's exhibits is based varies because not all units were able to supply answers to every survey question.

* Some refused patients may have been admitted to another unit with spare capacity, perhaps even within the same trust. On average, 5 per cent of admissions to units are transfers in from another unit. Conversely, the figures may underestimate demand if some doctors do not refer patients whom they think could benefit because they know the unit is full. Data are based on self-reports by critical care unit staff.

EXHIBIT 1B

Patients discharged early due to pressure on ICU beds**

...and others are discharged early to make room for new, higher priority patients.

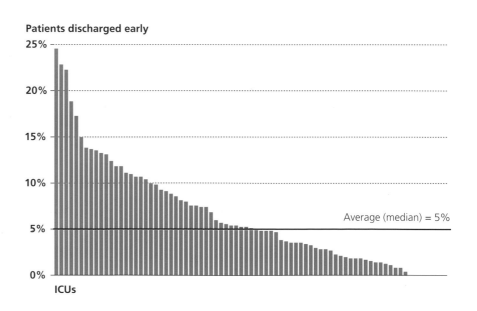

Patients discharged early

Average (median) = 5%

ICUs

** Defined by the Intensive Care National Audit & Research Centre (ICNARC) as 'an unplanned discharge for an admission still requiring the current level of care'.

Source: Audit Commission analyses of information from the ICNARC Case Mix Programme Database (79 units)

- *efficiency:* the cost per patient day, especially in nursing costs, unrelated to patient workload; and in the steps that units take to improve efficiency;
- *scale:* the number and size of units and beds;
- *configuration:* whether care is provided in specialist or generalist units, in separate or integrated intensive and high dependency care units, solely in critical care units or also in accident and emergency (A&E), admissions units, recovery and general wards; and
- *the place of critical care within the whole trust:* whether specialists in critical care, both doctors and nurses, are involved in training or care outreach to A&E, admissions units and the wards; whether the trust board has planned the place of critical care services within the trust as a whole.

5. The variation is due partly to the *ad hoc* development of services that has been described by the doctors involved as 'haphazard' (Ref. 2). Different specialties often develop separate units without joint planning. No single royal college oversees standards and, until very recently, there was no centrally agreed training curriculum. Few statistics on activity were collected in a standard format. Locally, the development money for critical care units has often been 'top sliced' by trusts from acute care contracts without the explicit agreement of purchasers and few contracts include service specifications or standards for critical care.

What the report aims to do

6. Faced with demand pressures and, in some cases, arrangements that do not offer the best value for money, trusts need to review and improve current services. The report [EXHIBIT 2, overleaf] aims to help by:
- showing how trusts can review information about the number of beds and units that they have and the patients for whom they provide care (Chapter 1);
- analysing variations in survival and the quality of life and describing how organisational arrangements can affect quality of care (Chapter 2);
- helping trusts to ensure that they are using resources – beds and staff – efficiently (Chapter 3); and
- finally, considering co-ordination and planning at trust board level. Once quality and efficiency have been improved, trusts can plan future capacity – the report explains the difficulties in deciding how many beds of different types to provide. Next, it reviews clinical governance issues (Chapter 4).

7. Different readers may wish to give certain sections of the report priority.
- *The public* will be especially interested in Chapter 1, which explains what critical care is, and the first two sections of Chapter 2, which describe different outcomes for patients.
- *The clinicians and managers* who provide, run and refer to critical care services will be most interested in how they compare with other

hospitals (Chapter 1) and in the detailed findings of Chapters 2 and 3 about how to improve quality and efficiency.

- *Trust boards and commissioning bodies* can use Chapter 1 to help to understand how their services are configured. They will be interested in the main messages of Chapters 2 and 3 and will wish to assure themselves that those providing and running the services are pursuing any improvements in quality and efficiency that are needed. The key messages for this audience are brought together in Chapter 4.

EXHIBIT 2

A map of the report

The report is structured to help trusts to review the configuration of critical care services, improve quality and efficiency and plan future services.

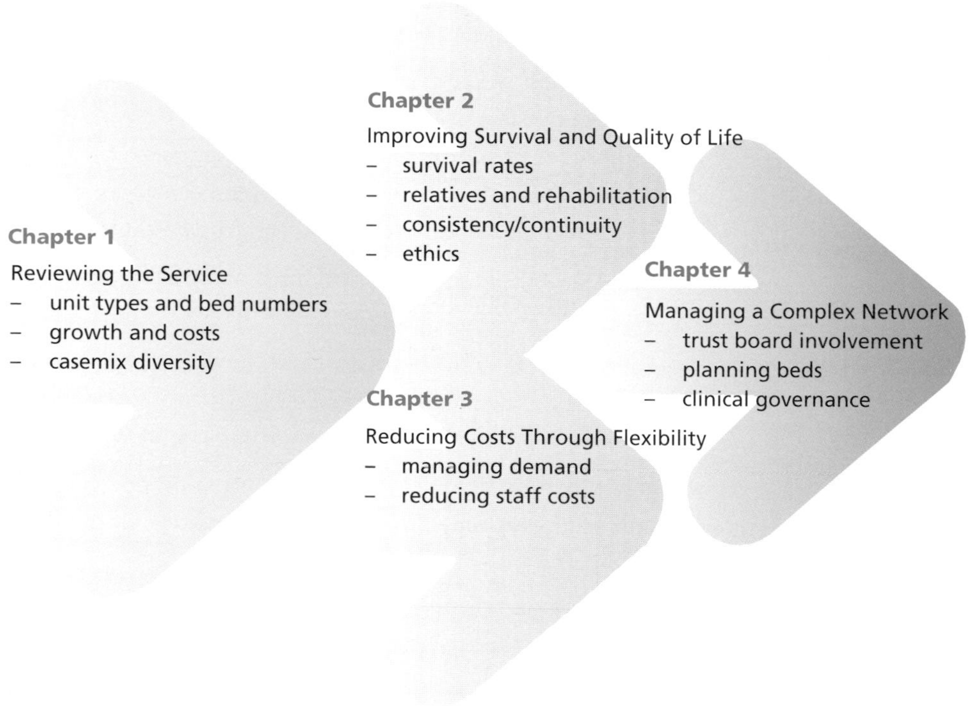

Chapter 2

Improving Survival and Quality of Life
- survival rates
- relatives and rehabilitation
- consistency/continuity
- ethics

Chapter 1

Reviewing the Service
- unit types and bed numbers
- growth and costs
- casemix diversity

Chapter 4

Managing a Complex Network
- trust board involvement
- planning beds
- clinical governance

Chapter 3

Reducing Costs Through Flexibility
- managing demand
- reducing staff costs

Source: Audit Commission

1

Reviewing the Service

On average, 1 per cent of acute beds are within general adult critical care units, rising to just over twice that when specialty-specific units are included. However, these ratios vary widely between trusts. The number of these expensive beds is growing quickly and the casemix of patients within them varies greatly.

8. Before trusts plan critical care, they should understand the make-up of their current service. Clinicians, managers and non-executive directors all need information. This chapter helps by explaining what critical care is, what it costs and how trusts differ in service configuration. It also profiles the types of patient (casemix) admitted to critical care units – the specialties that they originate from, the mix of planned and emergency admissions and how ill they are.

What critical care is and how it is organised

9. Critical care has developed rapidly over the second half of this century [BOX A]. Some doctors now specialise in it. Their specialism concerns the whole body's functions when a patient becomes critically ill. This matches the training and experience provided by anaesthesia and general medicine, the specialties from which most consultants working in general adult ICUs and HDUs originate, with the majority coming from anaesthesia. To date, critical care medicine has not been recognised as a separate specialty. But the Specialist Training Authority has now accepted the Intercollegiate Board for Training's recommendation that intensive care medicine be accepted as a specialty with dual accreditation with its parent specialty (that is, anaesthesia, general medicine, general surgery, etc). Clinicians also come together under the auspices of the Intensive Care Society, the Association of Anaesthetists, the British Association of Critical Care Nurses and the Royal College of Nursing Critical Care Forum to develop and publish clinical and organisational guidelines.

10. The average six-bedded general ICU, based on information from the Audit Commission survey, has 47 nurses (33.5 whole-time equivalents – WTEs), three consultants with fixed commitments to the unit, and three more taking part in the on-call rota. There is a trainee anaesthetist on duty throughout the 24 hours (some units take trainees from other specialties). This average unit also has a dedicated ward clerk, and shares a business manager, secretary, domestic staff, a technician and an audit clerk with other areas of the hospital. There is one WTE physiotherapist – several people usually contribute to these hours – and a smaller input from dieticians, occupational therapists, pharmacists and other specialist clinical staff. Outside the unit, there are many more doctors, nurses and other staff who refer patients, take patients after discharge, or provide services and support while patients are on the unit. Thus, the delivery of critical care services to patients involves a complex network of interactions between many people working within the hospital [EXHIBIT 3, overleaf].

BOX A

What is critical care?

In the 1950s in Denmark, a polio outbreak meant that there were too many patients for the few 'iron lungs' available at the time. Doctors instead transferred a technique in use in the operating theatre to support patients in respiratory failure. Air was blown directly into the lungs, and this technique became the forerunner of today's ventilators. This innovation almost halved the death rate. It soon led to the creation of specially equipped areas, with staff constantly looking after individual patients. Development of critical care services has since been rapid, and now includes the resuscitation, stabilisation and support of patients with many different kinds of system failure.

Most patients needing critical care are placed in central units where they can benefit from both higher staffing levels and staff with special skills. Centralisation also reduces duplication of costly equipment. Some patients need critical care because of an accident, others because of major illness. Some need it because they have had a major operation that leaves their bodies unable to function without support as they recover. Sometimes they need it for only a short period while doctors initiate treatments that help them to recover the ability to breathe and function for themselves. Others need support for a long time.

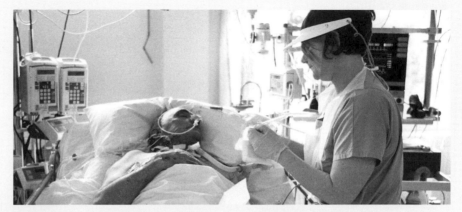

According to both the Department of Health and the Intensive Care Society, critical care services are intended for the most ill patients in the hospital who have potentially recoverable conditions. Critical care includes both:

- *intensive care:* the highest level of care which patients need when two or more of the body's vital life processes fail; and

- *high dependency care*: an intermediate level for, for example, patients who no longer need intensive care but who are not yet well enough to return to an ordinary ward, or those recovering from major surgery who need close monitoring.

Often, intensive care patients are unable to breathe on their own. They are kept under sedation so that a ventilator (that is, a 'breathing machine') can breathe for them by pushing air into the lungs. A tube is passed down the throat via the mouth or nose (intubation) or through a hole in the neck (tracheostomy). The ventilated patient cannot speak, but may be able to hear what is happening. Patients frequently need support for other organ systems (for example, their heart and circulation) and receive constant nurse presence. High dependency patients need support for a single failing system, or more general support or observation than can be provided on a ward or in the theatre recovery room. It is not usual for them to be ventilated, but they may be linked to a device that gives some help by 'topping up' their breathing.

It is high technology care, saving lives even when faced with the extremes of illness and injury. Although many lives are saved, death is a frequent occurrence and this, together with the appearance of the patient and the equipment, makes critical care units stressful places for patients, relatives and staff alike.

Source: Audit Commission, based on Department of Health (Ref. 5), Intensive Care Society (Ref. 6), Lassen (Ref. 7) and site visits

EXHIBIT 3

The main hospital clinical staff involved in caring for critical care patients

The delivery of critical care services to patients involves a complex network of interactions between many people working within the hospital.

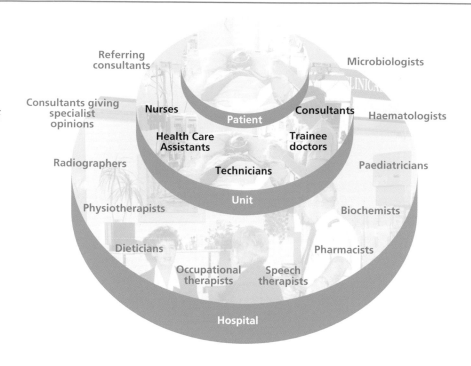

Source: Audit Commission

Beds and units

11. Nine out of every ten acute trusts have a 'general ICU', sometimes including high dependency or coronary care as well as intensive care beds. Some have separate high dependency units (HDUs) or specialty-specific units [**EXHIBIT 4**]. Most critical care beds are in general, mixed specialty units. On average, 1 per cent of acute hospital beds are designated for general critical care, but this varies widely, with the top quarter of trusts having more than twice the percentage of the bottom quarter. The same wide variation is found if specialist beds are included, with the average rising to just over 2 per cent. There are no significant differences in provision between trusts of different types [**EXHIBIT 5, overleaf**].

12. There is also no consistency in whether trusts have created few or many, small or large units. Some trusts have a large number of specialist units, managed by different clinical directorates. By contrast, other trusts bring these specialties into general units. For example, one teaching trust provides acute services from two hospitals containing eighteen separate critical care units. By contrast, a slightly larger teaching trust, despite operating from three hospitals, has two large, mixed-specialty, ICU/HDUs, with only a further five specialist units. Although this variation will partly reflect differences in the medical and surgical services offered by the two trusts, it also reflects different degrees of centralisation.

EXHIBIT 4

The number of critical care units and available beds of different specialties in England and Wales in 1998.

Most critical care beds are in general, mixed specialty units.

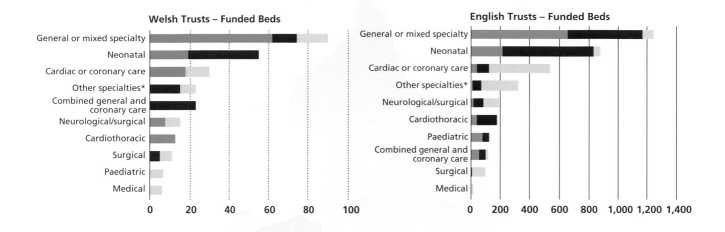

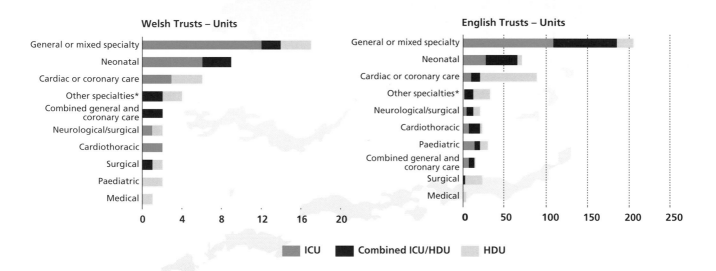

* For example, renal, burns, plastics, liver, spinal injuries.

Source: Audit Commission survey (227 trusts, England & Wales)

EXHIBIT 5

Variation in the number of critical care beds per 500 acute hospital beds

On average, just over 10 per 500 acute hospital beds (2 per cent) are designated for general and specialist critical care, but there is wide variation about this average and no significant differences in provision between trusts of different types.

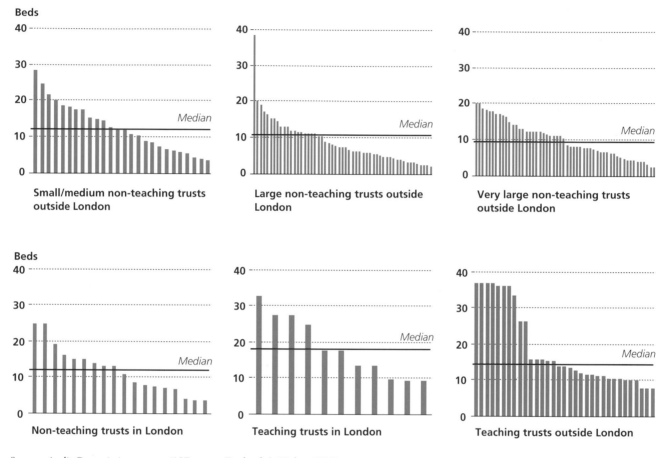

Source: Audit Commission survey (187 trusts, England & Wales, 1998)

Casemix

13. The previous section has described how trusts vary in the degree to which they create *general* units that take all kinds of patients or have some separate, specialist, units. The remainder of the report concentrates on general units and integrated general/specialist units (for example, general ICUs that are combined with a CCU). The first step to understanding these general units is to profile the patients that they admit. Although all general units have – by definition – a diverse casemix, they differ greatly from one another in the details. They vary in at least six key ways that affect quality, bed management and staffing (which are analysed in Chapters 2 to 4).

• Patients come to general ICUs from all over the hospital [EXHIBIT 6]. Units vary from admitting 10 per cent of their patients from theatre to 72 per cent, depending largely on whether major surgery is carried out in the hospital; and from a few per cent from A&E to 44 per cent, depending on the location of the hospital. These differences affect the best configuration of units for a trust and how many staff are involved in the communications network.

EXHIBIT 6

The source of patients admitted to the 'average' general ICU

Patients come to general ICUs from all over the hospital.

Source: Audit Commission analyses of information from the ICNARC Case Mix Programme Database (75 units)

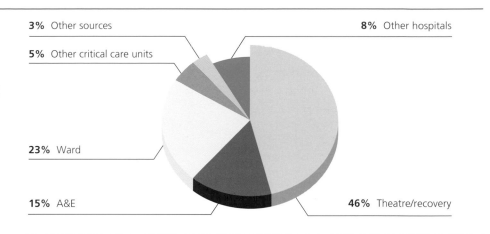

3% Other sources

8% Other hospitals

5% Other critical care units

23% Ward

15% A&E

46% Theatre/recovery

- On average, one-quarter of patient admissions are planned (for example, arriving on the unit after a planned operation) and three-quarters are unexpected emergencies (for example, arriving after a road accident, stroke or overdose) but these proportions are reversed for some units at the extremes [**EXHIBIT 7, overleaf**]. These differences affect the degree to which workload peaks and troughs can be predicted in advance, and how difficult it is to staff units appropriately.

- Even something as basic as the percentage of patients who are classified as surgical or other specialties (of which the majority are medical) varies greatly [**EXHIBIT 8, overleaf**]. And units admit patients with a wide range of differing primary illnesses [**EXHIBIT 9, overleaf**]. On average, cardiovascular problems are the primary reason for admitting one in every four patients. But the most common single condition – aortic aneurysm[I] – accounts for only 7 per cent of admissions, while pneumonia is the primary admission reason for 13 per cent of occupied bed days.[II] The degree of casemix diversity affects, for example, the range of training and experience needed by staff.

- Many patients have accompanying illnesses and a history of serious past illnesses – indeed, many patients are so seriously ill that, in addition to the condition which has been the main reason for coming into hospital, they have two or more other main organ systems in failure. The complex mix of illnesses makes it more difficult to decide whether admission to a unit is appropriate and affects the efficiency with which beds are managed.

I   The most common condition on average across this sample of units; some hospitals do not take patients with this condition at all.

II   Source: ICNARC Case Mix Programme Database.

15

EXHIBIT 7

Variation between units in the percentage of patients classified as emergency admissions

On average, one-quarter of patient admissions are planned and three-quarters are unexpected emergencies, but these proportions are reversed for some units at the extremes.

Source: Audit Commission survey (208 units, England & Wales, 1997/98)

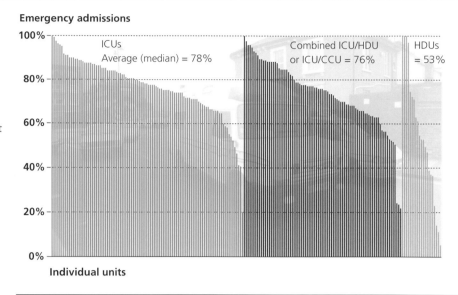

Emergency admissions

ICUs Average (median) = 78%

Combined ICU/HDU or ICU/CCU = 76%

HDUs = 53%

Individual units

EXHIBIT 8

Variation between critical care units in patients classified as surgical admissions

Even something as basic as the percentage of patients who are classified as surgical or other specialties (of which the majority are medical) varies greatly.

Source: Audit Commission survey (209 units, England & Wales, 1997/98)

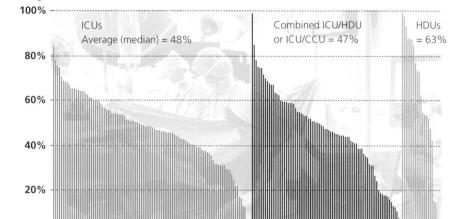

Surgical admissions

ICUs Average (median) = 48%

Combined ICU/HDU or ICU/CCU = 47%

HDUs = 63%

Individual units

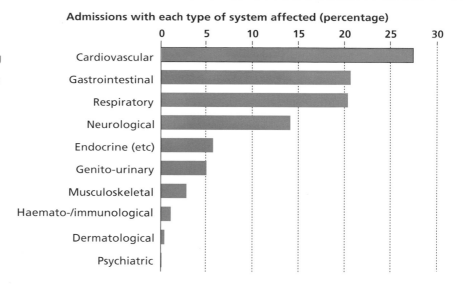

EXHIBIT 9

The primary illnesses of patients admitted to the 'average' general ICU

General units admit patients with a wide range of differing primary illnesses; cardiovascular problems are the primary reason for admitting one in every four patients.

Source: Audit Commission analyses of information from the ICNARC Case Mix Programme Database (79 units)

- Patients differ greatly in how ill they are, as measured both by the number of organ systems in failure (Chapter 3) and in the severity of their illness. Severity is not related to the size of the unit in a straightforward way – small ICUs are as likely to admit very ill patients as large units [**EXHIBIT 10, overleaf**]. Thus, it cannot be assumed that larger units receive the most ill patients who have been sent on from units in smaller hospitals, and therefore automatically need higher staffing levels and other resources.

- Doctors differ in the type of interventions that they employ. For example, there is wide variation in the proportion of patients that is ventilated in units labelling themselves as ICUs (Chapter 3). This variation is partly due to differing needs, but also to differing clinical judgements. The differences affect the efficient use of resources and perhaps quality of care.

Growth

14. As the population changes and medical advances provide the opportunity to treat more patients, demand pressures grow. Supply is mediated by commissioning bodies and trusts when they decide how to assign limited resources between competing priorities. Critical care provision has been increasing over a period when, according to government statistics, the overall number of hospital beds has been declining in both England and Wales.

- The number of HDUs has grown. In 1988, 23 per cent of hospitals had HDUs (Ref. 2). Within a decade this had risen to 45 per cent (Ref. 8).

- Although the number of general ICUs hardly changed between 1993 (the time of the last comprehensive survey) and 1998, the median number of beds within them rose from four (Ref. 3) to six.[1]

I   This comparison is based on a similar definition of available beds.

EXHIBIT 10

Variation in how ill patients are within general ICUs

Patients differ greatly in how ill they are, but small units are as likely to admit very ill patients as large units.

* The higher the Acute Physiology And Chronic Health Evaluation (APACHE II) score, the more severely ill a patient is.

Source: Audit Commission survey (70 units describing themselves as general ICUs, England & Wales, 1997/98)

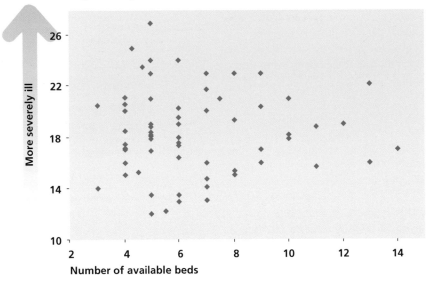

Average severity of illness (mean APACHE II score*)

More severely ill

Number of available beds

Costs

- The number of staff within ICUs has grown. For example, the number of nurses classified as working in intensive care nearly doubled during the 1980s, compared with only a 15 per cent growth in the number of all types of nursing during the same period (Ref. 9). And the number of consultant sessions has grown (Chapter 3).

15. In addition to the cost of growth, critical care is very expensive compared with most health care because of the higher staffing, monitoring and therapeutic inputs. In 1995/96 the average cost per patient day in 11 ICUs was estimated at £1,000 (Ref. 10) and case studies show that an intensive care patient can cost six times more per day than a ward patient, and a high dependency patient twice as much (Ref. 11). According to a recent estimate (Ref. 12), the annual UK bill for intensive care is £675-725 million, increasing at 5 per cent a year. The Audit Commission's new information about growth in bed numbers and unit costs (staffing levels, equipment and drug costs per bed have all increased – Chapter 3 and (Ref. 10)) suggests that in fact costs may be growing at double this rate.

16. A recent study has calculated detailed unit costs for critical care patients [EXHIBIT 11]. Rather than duplicate these efforts, the Audit Commission has concentrated on the biggest overall cost block – nursing staff. Audit Commission survey findings estimate that the average general ICU bed cost £120,000 to nurse during the financial year 1997/98. But there is great variation in this between units. In Chapter 3, overall nursing costs are broken down into their component parts and comparative information is used to help trusts to recognise where their particular problems lie.

EXHIBIT 11

The average components of cost in 11 general critical care units in 1995/96

The main component of costs is nursing staff.

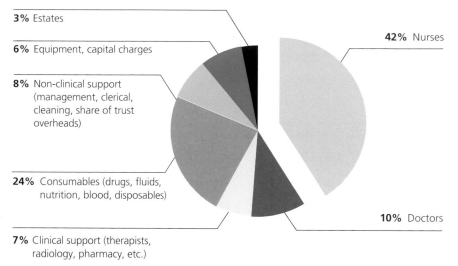

3% Estates

6% Equipment, capital charges

8% Non-clinical support (management, clerical, cleaning, share of trust overheads)

24% Consumables (drugs, fluids, nutrition, blood, disposables)

7% Clinical support (therapists, radiology, pharmacy, etc.)

42% Nurses

10% Doctors

Source: Edbrooke et al (Ref. 10)

17. This chapter has explained what critical care is, how heterogeneous services are and how much they cost in the round. Comparing quality of care and efficiency might be simple if the biggest units were found in the biggest hospitals, containing the most ill patients. They would straightforwardly need more beds and staff and have higher expected mortality. But this chapter has shown that the real situation is much more complex. The next two chapters break down some of the components of quality and efficiency and explain how trusts can use casemix and other information to compare their performance.

2

Improving Survival and Quality of Life

Trusts should consider quality of life as well as survival rates. The ethical and practical difficulty of conducting randomised controlled trials means that there is no evidence base for most critical care medicine. Ways to ensure consistency and continuity of care are needed. Few trusts have explicit policies to guide and support doctors who make ethical decisions about withdrawing or refusing critical care.

Most attention has focused on how many of the patients entering critical care units live or die. But the quality of life for those who survive is also important

18. Most attention has focused on how many of the patients entering critical care units live or die. In an area of medicine with high mortality, this emphasis is both understandable and desirable. But the quality of life for those who survive is also important [EXHIBIT 12, overleaf] (Ref. 13). And because the illnesses are so severe, some of the interventions used to tackle them are inherently dangerous. Sometimes harm can come as well as intended benefits, and the relative balance of harm and benefit is often less than clear cut. For example, the use of human albumin solution may (Ref. 14) – or may not (Ref. 15) – increase mortality risk. And the side-effects of long-term sedation include distorted memory, thirst and anxiety due to an inability to communicate. As these have become better known and techniques improve, most clinicians are seeking to reduce the depth of sedation (Ref. 16).

19. These factors – high mortality, quality of life restrictions and inherent dangers – mean that quality in critical care units matters as much as anywhere else in the hospital. Yet survival rates vary, the evidence base about why patients live or die is weak and few units actively follow up survivors' progress. This chapter examines why this is the case and what can be done about it. It shows that the way consultants organise themselves is associated with survival, and describes how some units try to ensure consistency and continuity of care. Finally, the chapter examines how quality and efficiency are inextricably linked in ways that raise ethical questions.

Survival

20. On average, more than one of every five ICU patients die on the unit, rising to nearly one in three when subsequent deaths on the wards are included, such is the severity of illness of many patients [EXHIBIT 12, overleaf]. In some ICUs, as many as three out of every five patients die. Although these rates are lower in combined units and HDUs, they still exceed those in most other areas of the hospital. For staff, this means the stress and sadness of seeing many of their patients die, and the presence of grieving relatives and friends. For patients and relatives, it means that the hope generated by admission to a unit will not necessarily be met – many people have unrealistic expectations of what critical care can achieve.

EXHIBIT 12

Different kinds of outcome for critical care patients

Most attention has focused on how many of the patients entering critical care units live or die. But the longer-term quality of life for those who survive is also important, as this example of ICU* patients shows.

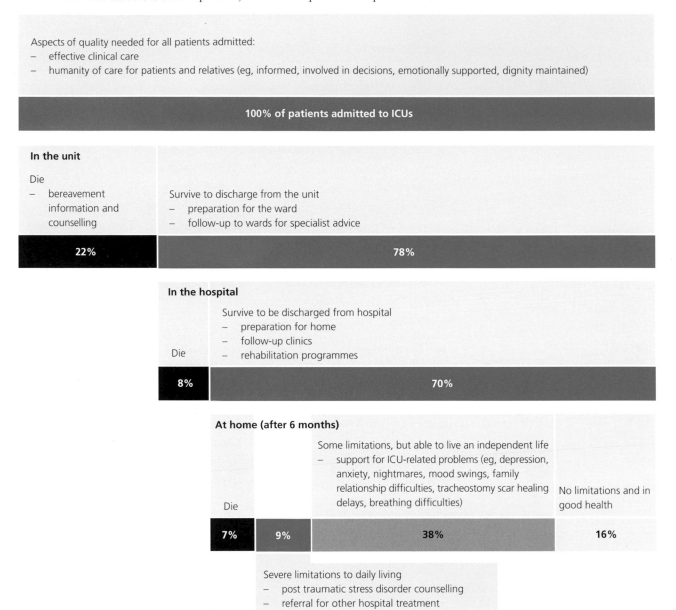

Aspects of quality needed for all patients admitted:
– effective clinical care
– humanity of care for patients and relatives (eg, informed, involved in decisions, emotionally supported, dignity maintained)

100% of patients admitted to ICUs

In the unit

Die
– bereavement information and counselling

Survive to discharge from the unit
– preparation for the ward
– follow-up to wards for specialist advice

22%   78%

In the hospital

Survive to be discharged from hospital
– preparation for home
– follow-up clinics
– rehabilitation programmes

Die

8%   70%

At home (after 6 months)

Some limitations, but able to live an independent life
– support for ICU-related problems (eg, depression, anxiety, nightmares, mood swings, family relationship difficulties, tracheostomy scar healing delays, breathing difficulties)

No limitations and in good health

Die

7%   9%   38%   16%

Severe limitations to daily living
– post traumatic stress disorder counselling
– referral for other hospital treatment

* The mortality rates for combined ICU/HDUs are 16 per cent (in unit) and 20 per cent (in hospital); and for HDUs 6 per cent (in unit) and 9 per cent (in hospital). Post-hospital mortality and quality of life percentages are not available for these patients.

Sources: Audit Commission survey and Rowan (Ref. 17)

21   The variation in survival rates between units largely reflects differences in casemix. But detailed work by the Intensive Care National Audit & Research Centre (ICNARC), and similar programmes commendably set up at the instigation of critical care clinicians themselves, show that some units have higher death rates than expected, even when complex adjustments are made for casemix [EXHIBIT 13]. Some care must be taken

EXHIBIT 13

Casemix-adjusted mortality in ICUs

Some units have higher death rates than expected, even when careful adjustment is made for casemix.

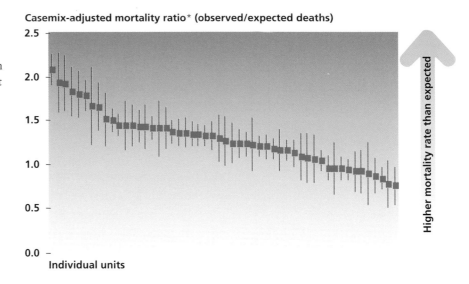

Casemix-adjusted mortality ratio* (observed/expected deaths)

Individual units

Higher mortality rate than expected

*   The squares plot the average mortality ratio for each unit's sample of patients. The bars show the variability about the average (+/- 95 per cent confidence limits). Two units have significantly different casemix-adjusted survival rates if these bars do not overlap – that is, one performs better than the other – and the difference is unlikely to be due to chance. Some care must be taken when interpreting these results, since the casemix-adjustment method is still being developed [Appendix 3].

Source: Audit Commission analyses of data from the ICNARC Case Mix Programme Database (52 units)

when interpreting these results, since the casemix-adjustment methods are still being developed and tested (Appendix 3).

Why survival rates vary

22. Given that survival rates vary between units even when patient differences are taken into account, the likelihood is that differences in clinical approach also affect survival. Such differences could be due to many things, ranging from individual choice of approach through to the amount of time available for each patient or the equipment and drugs available for use. However, by contrast with the detailed comparative information about patients' illnesses available via ICNARC and other programmes, there is a lack of routinely collected information about what interventions are used. Some units do not know basic facts – for example, how many patients are ventilated – because they do not extract information routinely from written notes. And even for those that use a common system to record interventions – the Therapeutic Intervention Scoring System (TISS) – the many different variants of the system prevent valid comparison. Concerted efforts should be made to standardise recording of interventions, paralleling the way that ICNARC is seeking to standardise casemix information.

23. Although information about treatment approaches is lacking, the Audit Commission survey does provide information about staffing resources and some aspects of organisation, which can be analysed in relation to survival. This reveals no relationship of survival rates to doctor

Poorer survival rates than expected are significantly more likely in units where each doctor works a set number of sessions every week

or nurse staffing levels or skill mix. However, a link was found with the way in which consultants cover the unit. Most commonly, each doctor works a set number of sessions every week (for example, every Tuesday morning and afternoon). The most frequent alternative is for one consultant to work solidly on the unit for a week, and then work elsewhere for two or more weeks. Poorer survival rates than expected are significantly more likely in units where each doctor works a set number of sessions every week [EXHIBIT 14].

24. It is unusual to discover an association between organisational factors and survival (Appendix 4). Without a controlled trial, it is impossible to say for certain whether the link is one of direct cause and effect. It does not follow that changing to a week on/weeks off system will automatically improve outcomes – some units where each doctor works a set number of sessions every week perform equally as well. The most frequent reason suggested during interviews is that treatment approaches differ in some of the units where doctors work the same sessions each week. Doctors and nurses often said during interview that treatments for patients with similar conditions vary from unit to unit – and even within units, especially if there are no guidelines to follow. Anecdotally, there are differences between doctors in the use of some of the most common interventions – some consultants are characterised by a tendency to intervene, while others have what their colleagues call a 'laissez-faire' approach.

25. These differences in treatment approach may, in turn, be linked to the consultant cover system. Some interviewees suggested that poorer performance is more likely if consultants do not have enough sessions to develop or maintain sufficient expertise in critical care medicine. This may be less likely under a week on/weeks off system, since each of the consultants involved will be working a solid week at regular intervals.

EXHIBIT 14

The type of consultant cover system and casemix-adjusted survival

Poorer survival rates than expected are significantly more likely in units where each doctor works a set number of sessions every week.*

* The difference between the two systems is statistically significant (p < 0.01). Four units with different systems (for example, no designated cover) have been excluded.

Source: Audit Commission survey; analyses of data from the ICNARC Case Mix Programme Database (46 units)

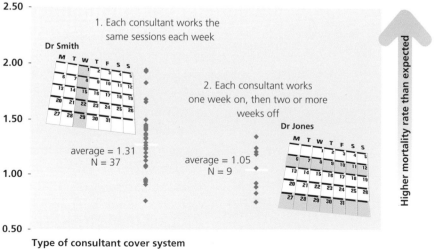

Casemix-adjusted mortality ratio

1. Each consultant works the same sessions each week

2. Each consultant works one week on, then two or more weeks off

average = 1.31
N = 37

average = 1.05
N = 9

Type of consultant cover system

Higher mortality rate than expected

26. Whether survival rates are good under the different types of consultant cover system may also depend on how the systems are implemented. Both the main systems have pros and cons [TABLE 1, overleaf]. For example, having individual sessions at the same time each week can risk continuity of care and may mean that patients' treatments are not progressed and that decisions are deferred. But units that are aware of this risk can take steps to counteract it – for example, by specifying that treatment progression will be a regular issue for discussion when handover occurs between consultants. Whichever system a unit chooses, all the possible risks to consistency of approach and continuity of care should be discussed and how they can be overcome agreed.

Improving the research base

27. Clinicians vary in their treatment approaches partly because there is a lack of scientific information about which interventions are effective, beyond the obvious life-saving effects of the immediate resuscitation phase. The need for more research into the relative costs and benefits of common ICU interventions was recognised ten years ago (Ref. 18). But many patients have multiple clinical conditions, complex case histories and complicated drug regimens already in place. There are so many factors impinging on survival and longer-term quality of life that it is hard to control for each of them during research. In addition, there is an ethical dimension that makes study design difficult. For example, interventions such as intracranial pressure monitors and haemofiltration units have been introduced into many ICUs over the years, despite a lack of scientific evidence demonstrating a survival benefit. But the professional consensus is that they are of benefit. These interventions are now so routinely used that denying them to some patients during a controlled trial could be considered unethical (Ref. 19).

28. Nevertheless, more effort should be put into researching why patients live or die, and the long-term effects of critical care on quality of life, to foster improvements. Indeed, a trial of one commonly used procedure (pulmonary artery catheterisation) is now thought ethical because of growing evidence suggesting higher mortality (Ref. 20). Given the nature of critical care, such research will largely require multi-site joint ventures.

29. These findings are of significance given the new clinical governance requirements on trusts to account for the quality of clinical care (Chapter 4). Participation in the ICNARC programme – or similar audit – is voluntary and units that do not take part may have above-average death rates without knowing it. ICNARC has no executive power – it can only draw adverse results to a unit's attention. Thus, despite the programme running since 1995, no major attention has been directed at particular units on the basis of their clinical results. This is partly because the casemix-adjustment methods are still being refined (Appendix 3). But, given that the ICU is an area of the hospital with high death rates, and where some of the most costly care takes place, this lack of action is undesirable. Trust boards and purchasers should make themselves aware of their unit's performance – which will mean investing in an appropriate audit framework – and renewed efforts should be directed at improving the casemix method and the evidence base.

TABLE 1

Patterns of cover by consultants

	Units			Pros	Cons
	ICUs	ICU/ HDU or ICU/CCU	HDUs		
Each consultant works the same sessions each week	76%	67%	10%	• Range of views on patient treatment readily available • Rota planning for off-unit commitments is easier • May be less demanding for the individual consultants • More varied learning opportunities for trainees • More chance for collective decision-making	• May risk continuity of care • Daily consultant-consultant handovers are needed to ensure continuity, which may require more consultant sessions in total • Treatments may not be progressed and decisions deferred • Daytime cover may include consultants with one or fewer daytime commitments to the unit
Each consultant works one week on, two or more weeks off, the unit	15%	13%	10%	• Continuity of care within the week • Only one consultant-to-consultant handover needed per week • More concentrated learning opportunities for trainees • Enables on-call rota to be shared only among consultants with daytime commitments to the unit • Reduces continual pressure on the lead clinician	• When off-duty for several weeks, consultants may lose touch with what is happening • Big learning curve for consultant on Monday morning • Big switch in treatment regimens may occur on Monday morning • May be too tiring/stressful for one consultant in the biggest, busiest units • May be more frequent on-call

Note: Units excluded from the table reported different systems, for example:

• some full-time intensivists plus others to cover on-call; or
• no designated sessions for cover – the admitting surgical and physician teams provide care, plus anaesthetists on-call (mostly HDUs).

Source: Audit Commission survey (237 general ICUs, ICU/HDUs, ICU/CCUs and HDUs, England & Wales, 1997/98)

Quality of life

30. The previous section has shown that survival rates vary. The other principal outcome of critical care – the quality of life for those that do survive – also varies. It is often said that patients, because of the severity of their illness and the degree of sedation used in most units, can remember nothing of their experience. However, the recollections of patients who attend follow-up clinics suggest that in fact they can remember – or worse – mis-remember [CASE STUDY 1]. In addition, visitors will experience the shock of seeing their relative connected to numerous

CASE STUDY 1

Patient awareness while under sedation

The photograph below is of a poster on the wall of an ICU that holds follow-up clinics. An ex-patient explained at a follow-up clinic that, while under sedation, he could hear his nurse open a fizzy drink can, but was unable to communicate how the sedative drugs were making him very thirsty ('I was thirsty. Hearing a can of coke being opened was torture knowing that it was not for me'). As a result of learning this from the follow-up clinic, the nurses are now more sensitively attuned to what their patients are experiencing and have changed their practice accordingly.

Another patient described how, as sedation was lifted but she remained ventilated, communication was difficult because 'everyone spoke too fast and I had insufficient time to respond … One nurse suggested a system of hand squeezes to indicate yes and no'. This patient also described how disturbing the noises of the unit can be while under partial sedation. 'The nurse explained each procedure to me, but they did not help interpret the distorted noises of ICU life.'

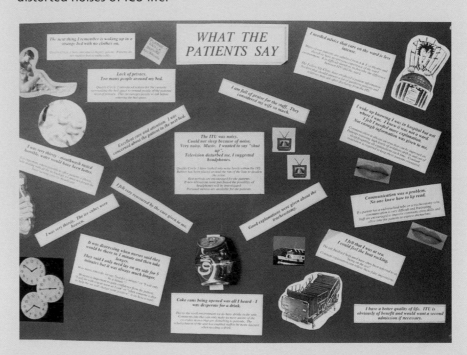

Source: Audit Commission site visit; Waldmann & Gaine [Ref. 21] *and Rosenthal* [Ref. 22]

pieces of bewildering equipment and may spend long periods within the unit. Their needs range from the basics, such as access to food at convenient times and a place to stay nearby, through to information on the patient's treatment and progress. They may also need help to come to terms with what happened during their vigil. And, after discharge, longer-term quality of life for patients and relatives can be adversely affected. This section considers how well units respond to psychological and physical needs, using the examples of care for relatives, children and the rehabilitation of survivors.

Care for relatives

31. In most areas of medicine, relatives find out what is happening via the patient. But when in critical care many patients are unable to communicate, and so special consideration must be given to the care of relatives. This is compounded by the life and death environment. On arrival in the unit, relatives may be shocked and worried about the serious condition of the patient, and may not remember everything that is said to them, especially about the basic necessities that they will need during their stay. As the most basic requirement, each unit should have a booklet available for relatives that contains general information. Most units say they have such a leaflet, but fewer have the more specific leaflets described [TABLE 2]. Some units also have an information pack in the waiting room that shows pictures of the equipment used in the unit, explaining what it is for. One site visited had a special leaflet for children visiting the unit, written as an animal story with puzzles and pictures to colour in. In addition, verbal communication about each individual patient is crucial, including clinical staff telling relatives what is going on.

TABLE 2

Does the unit have written information leaflets that cover these matters?

Percentage of units answering 'yes'	ICUs	ICU/HDU or ICU/CCU	HDUs
A leaflet introducing the unit to relatives of newly admitted patients	91%	84%	71%
A leaflet that prepares patients for what to expect on arrival in the unit (for example, major elective surgical patients)	41%	40%	50%
A leaflet that prepares patients for what to expect after discharge	12%	10%	18%
A leaflet for bereaved relatives	91%	86%	74%
A leaflet about organ donation	68%	73%	44%
Number of units replying	*116*	*101*	*34*

Source: Audit Commission survey (England & Wales, 1997/98)

The most direct way for staff to find out whether their approaches to care are providing the support that patients and relatives need is to ask them in a systematic way

32. Death is such a common occurrence that helping bereaved relatives is a basic part of any ICU clinician's job. There are processes that can be put in place to help to support relatives. Many of these have been set out by the Intensive Care Society in a booklet for staff (Ref. 23). Beyond the provision of a leaflet for relatives [TABLE 2], other forms of help are less frequent. For example, only three in every five ICUs can offer a specialist counselling service.[1]

33. While the majority of units can offer the basic minimum standard of accommodation for relatives – a waiting room – one-third are unable to offer overnight accommodation near the unit [TABLE 3].

34. The most direct way for staff to find out whether their approaches to care are providing the support that patients and relatives need is to ask them in a systematic way. Some units already carry out satisfaction surveys. The Audit Commission has developed a relatives' satisfaction questionnaire, available to all units via their local auditors.

Children

35. It is sometimes necessary for general critical care units to admit young children. The 'average' unit admits two children under the age of 11 per year (8 under the age of 18), and these may be any age from babies upwards.[1] In a few general units, as many as 1 in 10 patients are children under the age of 11. Most are transferred after initial resuscitation and stabilisation to children's units. The Paediatric Intensive Care Society has suggested that special arrangements should be made when children are within general units (Ref. 24). Few general units meet these standards and are unlikely to be able to in the foreseeable future, given costs and the availability of staff with the required training [TABLE 4, overleaf]. In these

TABLE 3

Accommodation for the relatives of patients on critical care units

Percentage of units answering 'yes'	ICUs	ICU/HDU or ICU/CCU	HDUs
A waiting room on or adjacent to the unit	98%	95%	50%
A separate room where bad news can be given (apart from the sister's or doctor's office)	66%	67%	38%
Overnight accommodation on or adjacent to the unit	66%	75%	38%
Number of units replying	*116*	*101*	*34*

Source: Audit Commission survey (England & Wales, 1997/98)

[1] Source: Audit Commission survey.

TABLE 4

Children within general critical care units

Percentage of units answering 'yes'	ICUs	ICU/HDU or ICU/CCU	HDUs
Children that stay for longer than one day	61%	47%	12%
Key standards:*			
Continual immediate availability of medical staff with paediatric airway skills	66%	54%	24%
When a child is on the unit: 24-hour cover by a consultant who is experienced and trained in paediatric intensive care	28%	20%	12%
Consultant with a unit sessional commitment who has approved training in paediatric intensive care	17%	14%	3%
Registered children's nurse (RSCN) looks after each child throughout 24 hours	13%	12%	9%
A bed for children that is physically separated from areas for adults	45%	39%	6%
Parents can stay at the child's side at any time of the day or night	76%	71%	24%
Number of units replying	*116*	*101*	*34*

* Specified by the Paediatric Intensive Care Society (Ref. 24)

Source: Audit Commission survey (England & Wales, 1997/98)

circumstances, units should review current provision against these guidelines, prepare a plan with target dates for feasible improvements, and produce a written policy on when children should be transferred to specialist facilities.

Rehabilitation

36. The aim of critical care should be to restore patients as near as possible to their level of health before the event that led to their arrival (Ref. 25). But, as shown at the beginning of the chapter, three-quarters of ICU patients who are alive six months after leaving hospital have some limitations in daily living. There has been relatively little research directed at the long-term effects of the more intensive forms of care on those who survive to leave hospital. What has been done shows that many aspects of quality of life are adversely affected, including physical health, employment status, mental health and relationships with family members (Refs. 26 and 27).

A period in a critical care unit presents patients with particular difficulties later on. This applies especially to intensive care patients who have been sedated for ventilation

37. The process of rehabilitating survivors should begin before patients leave the critical care unit. Patients and relatives often comment on the big step-change they experience when discharged to the ward, moving from a constant nurse presence to having less time being given to them. Three-quarters of units say that their nurses visit the wards to advise on aspects of physical care and to ease the transition process. An explanation of what took place on the unit can be given in an atmosphere where it is more likely to be understood. Future fears and anxieties about what will happen can also begin to be addressed.

38. A 'goodbye' leaflet for patients and relatives can help them to prepare for the ward and for life at home afterwards, although few units currently have them (Table 2, page 28). Unit staff who wish to produce such leaflets will need to be clear about what they should contain. They are not intended to replace the information about patients' underlying conditions that is the responsibility of the admitting surgeon or physician. Rather, they should provide complementary information about those aspects that are especially introduced by critical illness, and about the psychological impact and practicalities of moving from an environment with a high degree of nurse, doctor and therapist contact to a much less intense environment.

39. Successful rehabilitation after discharge from the hospital requires careful assessment, planning and evaluation, which builds on the care that is planned and delivered when patients were in hospital. It therefore requires a joint effort between hospital and community staff. Too often this excludes critical care staff, yet it is becoming clear that a period in a critical care unit presents patients with particular difficulties later on, about which unit staff have specialised knowledge. This applies especially to intensive care patients who have been sedated for ventilation. GPs are relatively inexperienced in the problems that are specific to such patients because there are few on their lists at any one time. And follow-up programmes run by admitting consultants tend to concentrate on the specific surgical or medical problem that the patient was admitted to hospital for.

40. Without some kind of follow-up, the only outcome that critical care staff can gain knowledge about is whether their patients die or leave hospital alive. And without knowledge about subsequent quality of life, there is nothing on which to base improvements to the practice of critical care, except in terms of what affects survival. A few units (7 per cent) have established follow-up clinics for surviving patients and their relatives [CASE STUDY 2, overleaf]. The clinics serve both medical and psychological needs. For example, one study used information collected at clinics to find out that ex-patients experiencing severely restricted air flow had been reintubated several times when in the ICU. Patients who require frequent reintubation are now checked carefully at follow-up clinics (Ref. 28). Another study found a link between itching and the use of certain types of infusion (Ref. 29).

CASE STUDY 2

A follow-up clinic run by ICU staff

At one hospital, every surviving patient who stays longer than four days in the ICU is invited to return at two, six and twelve months after discharge. The system fulfills several functions:

Clinical: Staff record, for example, lung function and tracheostomy scar healing rates, which helps them to change their practice to ensure better long-term results for patients. A more clinically-trivial example, but one with implications for the humanity of care, was the finding that applying the pulse oximeter to one finger for a prolonged period was very painful, but sedated patients could not communicate this readily. Staff now regularly switch the oximeter between fingers. They can also identify patients who need referral on within the hospital for further treatment.

Psychological: Patients and their relatives who need counselling help are identified – 15 per cent of patients attending had clinically recognisable post traumatic stress disorder (characterised by intrusive thoughts, nightmares and intense distress when confronted by reminder triggers).

Humanity of care: Finding out what patients can remember helps staff to change their practice to benefit new patients. For example:

- staff learnt that patients may hear some of what is said at the bedside, but misinterpret it in frightening ways due to the sedative drugs; they now conduct most of the ward rounds and shift handovers in the office, followed by 'fine-tuning' clinical decisions at the bedside; and
- nurses who could lip-read were better able to understand the communication attempts of patients with intubation or tracheostomy tubes, leading to more staff receiving this training.

Relatives' experiences: Staff learn more clearly about the stresses on relatives, allowing them both to care better for the relatives of new patients and focus information leaflets on what relatives say is most important to them.

Resources: Being able to present systematic evidence from the clinics to the trust board has made the case for resources for, for example, better relatives' accommodation, more windows, a new clinical information system and a blood-gas analyser. External donations have also been generated.

Litigation: There is circumstantial evidence that potential lawsuits have been avoided because people have had the chance to talk through their concerns at a clinic.

Having initially funded the clinics from current resources, the money to follow up 50-80 patients a year is now identified by the trust as a separate budget item. The unit has estimated the annual cost of the clinic at £10,500, about 1 per cent of the unit's annual budget.

Source: Audit Commission site visit and Waldmann & Gaine (Ref. 21)

As with survival differences, there is a dearth of research into why quality of life varies

41. Some units link follow-up clinics to support groups. These help patients and their families who do not need specialist counselling but who are, nevertheless, finding it difficult to adjust psychologically [BOX B]. One ICU that is fostering such a group has found this of value for a wide range of patients who are suffering depression, anxiety, irritability and social isolation (Ref. 30).

42. While follow-up clinics, support groups and referral for counselling all help towards rehabilitation, one unit has gone further and designed a 90-page self-help manual. This is tailored to the problems that ex-critical care patients and their relatives experience, and guides them through their day-by-day rehabilitation over the first six weeks at home (Ref. 31). As with survival differences, there is a dearth of research into why quality of life varies. But this example shows how local research can improve efforts to rehabilitate patients. The package helps patients to set their own fitness and psychological targets and, after a period of complete dependence, begin to take control once more of their own future. It provides practical advice and plans for exercise, diet, anti-stress and relaxation techniques, what can be done when faced with mood swings or panic attacks, and other aspects of daily living. The exercises are interspersed with case studies, which are written in plain English and describe common psychological and physical problems that patients encounter, and how patients have tried to overcome them.

Approaches to care

43. The preceding sections have shown that the two main outcomes for critical care – survival and the quality of life of survivors – both vary between units. The lack of evidence as to which medical interventions help patients to survive means that trusts should concentrate on other factors likely to have an influence, such as the way in which staff organise themselves, the roles that they take on, and the philosophy of care that they adopt. This section considers two interacting key principles:

BOX B

Family rehabilitation

Because of their illness and sedation, many patients do not have a clear perspective on their experience, and may have unrealistic expectations about their recovery and rehabilitation. By contrast, relatives may be over-protective and do not expect rehabilitation because of their memories of how ill and dependent the patient has been. This means that families often need help in resolving conflicts between the differing experiences and expectations of patient and family. Follow-up clinics and support groups help in this regard and give both an understanding of what can be achieved and how to go about it.

Source: Audit Commission site visit and Jones (Ref. 31)

The critical care environment is a complex network involving many different people. Good communication skills and processes are needed

- *consistency*: when there is uncertainty about which interventions might lead to recovery, it is safest to adopt a consistent approach to care. Aiming for consistency fits with emerging concepts that doctors who work in teams should assume a more explicit collective responsibility for their standards of practice, and that such arrangements can form the basis for team-based self regulation within a supportive environment (Ref. 32). Consistency is especially important in critical care because of the many consultants and other staff involved in the care of each patient; and

- *continuity of care*: many different staff will care for even the shortest stay patients. Ways are needed to make sure that a change of personnel when a new shift starts does not mean that, for example, relatives receive conflicting messages or get forgotten because no one member of staff is clearly identified as being responsible for keeping them informed.

44. The section on survival has already shown that one aspect of organisation – the type of consultant rota system – is important. This section considers further key ways in which trusts can promote the two aims of consistency and continuity. They need to ensure that:

- communication is good between the multidisciplinary team and that, for each patient, an agreed and documented multidisciplinary care plan exists which everyone follows, and which is regularly reviewed and updated;

- systems for rostering nurses promote communication and agreement;

- there are agreed, written guidelines detailing the interventions that will be used in particular circumstances; and

- there are clearly agreed role definitions within the team and, in particular, a planned approach to the developing scope of nursing practice.

Multidisciplinary communication

45. The critical care environment is a complex network involving many different people. Good communication skills and processes are needed. The Audit Commission has developed questionnaires that can help trusts to 'take the temperature' of how well communication systems are working, and an ongoing, Europe-wide research project is also investigating these subtle aspects of critical care (Ref. 33). The structures that can promote effective communication are not unique to critical care units. Detailed consideration of each is outside the scope of this report, but will include adequate meeting arrangements, cascade arrangements for information and audit, combined with a strong sense of the need for multidisciplinary teamworking.

46. Of all the relationships between the many people involved in providing critical care, the way in which referring and specialist critical care doctors work together is one of the most important. There are two basic styles of medical management within critical care units:

- *closed*: the unit's doctors take responsibility for clinical management, with the patient's care formally transferred from the referring consultant; and

- *open*: patients remain under the care of their referring consultant with any unit doctors considered to be advisory (Ref. 6).

47. Closed systems are usual – in only 20 per cent of ICUs and ICU/HDUs do referring consultants initiate any of the care.[1] By contrast, in 80 per cent of HDUs most of the referring consultants initiate care. There is no strong evidence that either system is better for patients, although a series of single-site studies, mainly from the USA, suggest better outcomes for patients under a closed system which is staffed by doctors who specialise in critical care (Refs. 34, 35, 36 and 37). The degree to which a unit is open or closed need not threaten consistency providing that a treatment plan is agreed for each patient, that guidelines exist and that both plan and guidelines are followed. Problems arise if responsibilities are not clear and doctors start acting independently of one another. As one intensive care consultant stated: 'Sometimes people get better in spite of what you do, not because of it. We have no evidence base in intensive care. So it's dangerous as a doctor if you start to believe too strongly that people are getting better because of what you do and that alone. Then you begin to get arguments developing between team members, you can't get guidelines agreed, and don't review the evidence and options for each patient properly as a team' (Ref. 38).

Nursing systems

48. The 'named nurse' system has been a requirement for some years now, and many general hospital wards adopt either a team or primary nursing system as the profession's preferred way of achieving this (See Table 5 for a brief explanation of these terms) (Ref. 39). The objective is to improve the continuity and quality of nursing care. Few critical care units have adopted such systems [TABLE 5, overleaf]. The main reason is that patients automatically receive closer personal attention than does any patient on a general ward, because of higher staffing ratios. Additional reasons for a shift-by-shift allocation of nurses to each patient include:

- the match of nurses to patients' needs – since patients' needs change over time, it may be better to change to a nurse with experience and specialist knowledge that is suited to each stage;

- nurse 'burn-out' – after several shifts of working for the same patient, a nurse may feel that the patient would benefit from a fresh approach. Moreover, staying with the most stressful and difficult of patients on consecutive shifts may put too much strain on the nurse;

- the training and supervision needs of nurses are more easily met if nurses can be moved from patient to patient; and

- it is easier to plan the roster if nurses are allocated to patients on a shift-by-shift basis.

---

[1]   Source: Audit Commission survey, 193 units.

TABLE 5

Different ways of allocating nurses to patients within critical care units

The system that most typically describes the way that care is organised	ICUs	ICU/HDU or ICU/CCU	HDUs
Primary nursing (one named nurse who works with associates)	18%	21%	18%
Team nursing (a patient is nursed by only one team's members every day)	13%	8%	18%
Shift-by-shift allocation of nurses to patients	65%	65%	61%
A different system	4%	6%	3%
Number of units	*115*	*98*	*33*

Source: Audit Commission survey (England & Wales, 1997/98)

49. However, these reasons should all be accommodated within the principle of continuity, and not take precedence as a matter of course. A primary or team nursing system can work better in units that rotate or share staff between HDU and ICU. In one unit, named nurses follow their patients from ICU to the HDU, and then take responsibility for follow-up visits once the patient has been discharged to the ward.

Guidelines

50. Guidelines are 'systematically developed statements to assist decisions for practitioner and patient about appropriate healthcare for specific clinical circumstances' (Ref. 40). Given the lack of evidence about what interventions are effective, guidelines that are 'right' cannot be produced for critical care. However, in such circumstances it becomes even more important to have written guidelines in order to achieve consistency. Those involved should debate the alternative approaches and then agree on one. Not all clinicians will think it the best way, but in the interests of consistency agree to work to that guideline – 'this is how we will do it for now'. As new information becomes available, the guidelines should be reviewed and changed. Practice varies. Some units visited had no written guidelines, on the grounds that the multiple illnesses of many critical care patients made them unworkable. Others had a large number and regularly audited compliance.

The nurse role

51. The critical care unit is one of the main areas in the hospital where multidisciplinary teamworking is crucial, and where the nursing role is very advanced. Developments in critical care – especially in ICUs – are changing the nursing role by involving nurses more in decisions to alter treatment levels to maintain or attain desired goals (Ref. 41).

52. Changing the scope of nursing practice can limit demands on trainee doctors, which is important as their hours reduce. In one study of trainee doctor activity across a whole hospital, before the reduction in service commitment, six activities took up 16 per cent of trainee doctor time (Ref. 42). In the majority of critical care units, nurses have taken on these and other activities.[1] For example, in units where the nurses now take and analyse blood samples, the saving in time is substantial for the trainee doctor who in the past would have had to go round each patient and do them all. But there is a substantial minority of units that has yet to realise such advantages.[1]

53. And there may be quality benefits:

- more timely decision-making and action if the bedside nurse has a wider role. This avoids patients and anxious relatives listening to alarms beeping and waiting for a harassed trainee doctor to arrive **[CASE STUDY 3]**;

- improved continuity, more consistency and better technical quality if an experienced practitioner regularly undertakes an intervention, rather than a trainee doctor who may be very new to critical care; and

- the bedside nurse, as the member of staff most readily available to relatives, would be more informed, thus improving continuity of care.

CASE STUDY 3

Changing nurse responsibilities

A key aspect of the changing scope of nursing practice is that it is not just a gradual extension of technical abilities, but the adoption of a wider responsibility. For example, one nurse interviewed described some of the decisions that she had recently been taking. A complex patient had 15 infusions in place. She needed to titrate (that is, adjust to achieve a desired outcome) all of these and ensure that the combination remained safe. She knew that a drop in central venous pressure might cause a change to another system, and so altered a drip rate using her knowledge of how systems interact. Knowing that fluid restriction was needed, but that the patient was currently on a high flow rate of a sedative drug, she suggested that a more concentrated solution was needed to achieve both aims. Decisions that this nurse is not currently sanctioned to make include adjusting the fluid balance or administering (that is, effectively, prescribing) a different drug to alter blood pressure.

Source: Kite (Ref. 43).

1 Source: Audit Commission survey.

54. Extending nurse decision-making may also lead to shorter lengths of stay if earlier weaning from sedation and ventilation allows quicker discharge [CASE STUDY 4]. It may be easier to introduce first in units with a relatively uniform casemix (for example, cardiac units, where cost savings have been identified (Ref. 44)) because staff become especially familiar with particular problems.

55. Despite these potential benefits, the scope of nursing practice varies between units. For example, one-half of units contain nurses who can decide when it is time to wean a patient from ventilation. But in the remainder, weaning cannot proceed until a doctor is available to make the decision [EXHIBIT 15]. In all units, it remains the job of senior clinicians to ensure that, when required for the benefit of patients, decision-making is shared between doctors and nurses.

56. Such changes must be accompanied by good education, training and competency testing, and audited against quality standards. The proportion of nurses with post-basic qualifications varies between trusts [EXHIBIT 16, overleaf], but the average has changed little since 1991 when two-fifths held

CASE STUDY 4

Nursing responsibility for withdrawing breathing support can speed throughput

Consultants usually make extubation decisions (withdrawing breathing support) during a daytime session. It would be unreasonable to expect an on-call consultant to come into hospital at night just to do this, unless there was a severe bed crisis and choices had to be made quickly about which patients should be discharged. Thus, a patient who is ready for extubation in the night might wait until the next day for this to take place. If the nurse has been trained to make extubation decisions following guidelines, then extubation can occur during the night, and withdrawal of sedation may be begun half a day earlier. The potential resource consequences are large – although a few patients stay in the ICU for a very long time, the median length of stay is about two days. One USA study recently quantified the reduction in time spent on ventilators, and found no difference in safety (Ref. 45). There is likely to be a bigger impact in the 'fast-track' situations – for example, cardiac units – when each bed can be used more than once with only short gaps in between. And, in general units, the number of patients who fall within the guidelines for nurse decision-making will depend on the casemix – for complex cases, the decision to wean should follow a *team* discussion.

Source: Audit Commission site visits and Kolleff et al (Ref. 45)

38

relevant ENB or WNB qualifications (Ref. 9). The Intensive Care Society recommends, as a minimum, that 25 per cent of nurses should have the ENB 100 (specialist training in intensive care nursing) – or equivalent, allowing four-bed and larger units to roster at least one nurse per shift with the qualification (Ref. 6). Most units exceed this target, and some believe that the aim should be 100 per cent. There is no research evidence to show that having these qualifications leads to better outcomes, but most people would agree with the principle of having nurses with the right skills. Training is a key step towards achieving this objective.

EXHIBIT 15

The scope of nursing practice in critical care units

There is variation in the scope of nursing practice between units. For example, one-half of units contain nurses who can decide when it is time to wean a patient from ventilation. But in the remainder, a doctor must take this decision.

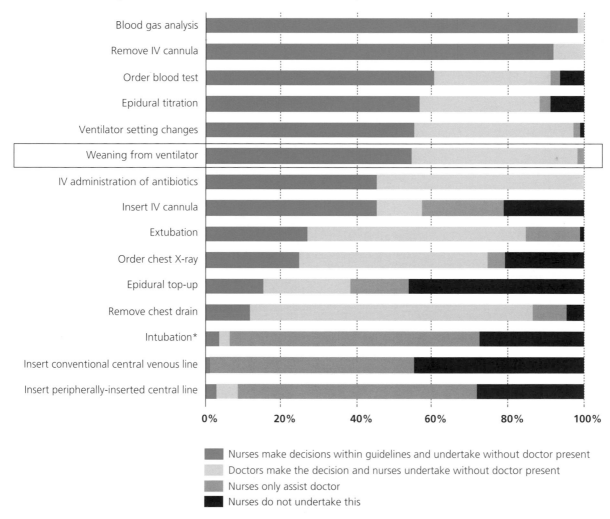

Nurses make decisions within guidelines and undertake without doctor present
Doctors make the decision and nurses undertake without doctor present
Nurses only assist doctor
Nurses do not undertake this

* That is, intubation is carried out as part of the emergency 'crash' team if no anaesthetist is present.

The exhibit shows example results from a list of 35 interventions for which information was collected. In each row, units that do not undertake the procedure are excluded.

Source: Audit Commission survey (213 ICUs, ICU/HDUs, ICU/CCUs and HDUs, England & Wales, 1997/98)

EXHIBIT 16

Variation in the percentage of critical care unit nurses that hold the ENB 100 (or equivalent) qualification in intensive care nursing

The Intensive Care Society recommends that a minimum of 25 per cent of nurses should have the ENB 100 (or equivalent) and most units exceed this target.

Source: Audit Commission survey (238 units, England & Wales, 1997/98)

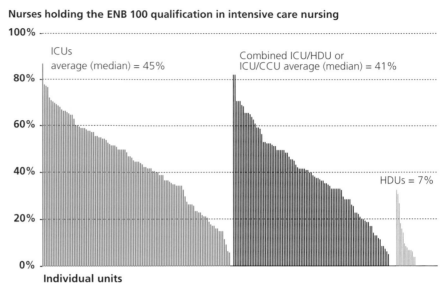

Nurses holding the ENB 100 qualification in intensive care nursing

57   In some US units that do not make use of trainee grade doctors to provide a service contribution, the nurse role has become that of 'case manager' [Ref. 46]. This development means that the nurse becomes responsible for directing and co-ordinating all aspects of the patient's healthcare during the ICU stay, under delegation from the consultant. No UK units have developed the bedside nurse role to this extent, although consultant doctors at some units visited said that as they perceive the availability and experience level of trainee doctors to be declining, they rely more on nurses to provide knowledge about such things as the patient's admission pathway. One unit director said that he could envisage a future situation where the trainee doctors were effectively supernumerary, and the service aspects of the unit were run as a consultant-nurse partnership.

58.   In the absence of a nationally agreed policy on the scope of nursing practice within critical care, each trust has to determine its own policy to ensure that changes are properly planned. Because of the effect of this on other staff groups, this policy should be discussed and agreed at unit level, rather than just within the nursing function. The policy should state the current scope, the scope that is aimed for, the timescales for change and the training and competency assessment that will back up the policy. The purpose of change should be stated, in terms of patient and resource benefits, and any effects on the mix of professions and grades that make up the critical care team should be explicitly stated.

Ethics

59.   So far this chapter has considered two key outcomes for patients – survival and quality of life – and what can help or hinder their achievement. The chapter ends by considering an aspect of equity that links quality and costs, and leads on to the next two chapters.

60. Most people would agree that critical care services should be available for all patients who can benefit. But there may be disagreement about who those patients are. Moreover, although critical care is often successful at saving and prolonging life, it can also prolong the process of dying. It is a major issue for the public and introduces ethical and legal difficulties when making decisions about refusing or withdrawing treatment from patients who are unlikely to recover.

Patients with poor prognosis

61. Those who make daily decisions may find it impossible to please, whatever they decide – 'when a relative is taken suddenly ill or sustains an accident there is a vague feeling that "everything possible should be done" and also unrealistic expectations about recovery. On the other hand, one also hears complaints of the loss of dignity suffered by patients who spend their last days linked up to tubes and unable to communicate with distressed relatives.'[1] Most of the units visited operated a decision-making policy of 'lowest common denominator' – that is, if any member of the multidisciplinary team was unsure about withdrawing treatment, then intervention would continue with another multidisciplinary review in 24 hours' time. These dilemmas mean that some patients who are admitted to units cannot benefit from intensive care [CASE STUDY 5, overleaf]. For other patients the admission is appropriate, but then a lack of guidelines or agreed approach allows them to stay without proper review beyond the point at which intervention could bring about recovery. Where there is uncertainty, both doctors and nurses may talk in terms of the 'torturing' of patients, whose suffering is prolonged by intervention without benefit (Audit Commission interviews and Ref. 43).

Guidance on ethical decisions

62. The experienced, lead intensive care clinician must frequently decide whose treatment should be withdrawn or who should be refused admission. But it is not appropriate to place such a decision-making burden on individual clinical staff without a supporting framework that is provided by the trust. As the examples above suggest, general guidelines will only partially help those who have to make decisions about individual complex cases. Nevertheless, guidelines are needed that:

- state where patients in need of long-term critical care or terminal care will be looked after (ICU should be for patients with potentially recoverable conditions);

- place limits on treatment for those patients for whom there is little hope of survival;

- cover the conditions under which treatment should be withdrawn; and

- make explicit the status of advanced directives ('living wills') and 'do not resuscitate' orders.

---

1   Source: letter received during the Audit Commission study.

CASE STUDY 5

Patients admitted to critical care units with poor prognosis

Case examples of patients where placement in a critical care unit is of debatable value

- An elderly man with pneumococcal pneumonia died in the unit. His condition was irreversible, but life could be prolonged by modern intensive care for a while. In the past such a patient would have died earlier, and perhaps with more dignity, elsewhere.

- A 70-year-old woman was admitted with chronic bronchitis. She had a small chance of 'recovery' if she spent 3-4 weeks on a ventilator. If she lived, her subsequent quality of life was likely to be very poor. The relatives at the beginning wanted resuscitation to take place. After a while they began to doubt whether treatment should continue, and perhaps wished that their relative had been allowed to die without further intervention on the ward.

- An elderly patient with breathing difficulties and 'low reserves' had a cardiac arrest on the ward, and was taken by the crash team to ICU for resuscitation and stabilisation. No 'do not resuscitate' order had been placed in the notes. The prognosis was very poor, and the patient died after several weeks in the unit. Her arrival on the unit was, as it were, a 'fait accompli'. The circumstances made admission inevitable, even though the eventual outcome was always likely to be death.

The resource consequences of admitting patients with a poor prognosis

- One clinical director pointed out that most patients admitted with three or more organs in failure die. He believed that a unit that admits high numbers of such patients is misusing resources, and should allow more of such patients to die without further intervention in a more suitable environment. According to survey returns, of the 103 units that collected information on organ failure, on average 12 per cent of patients within ICUs had three or more organs in failure, and one-quarter of units had 20 per cent or more such patients.

- A study in a large teaching hospital found that 4 per cent of 3,600 ICU patients were so ill that there was little hope of survival (95 per cent subsequently died within 90 days of discharge from hospital). But these patients consumed 17 per cent of the ICU's costs, due to longer lengths of stay and treatment costs [Ref. 47].

The difficulty facing doctors is that, had treatment been denied to the patients in the last example, one in twenty would have died who could have survived. Most people would not wish to accept such a risk.

Source: Audit Commission interviews with critical care unit doctors and Atkinson et al (Ref. 47)

63. In addition to agreeing guidelines, some hospitals refer the most difficult or controversial individual cases to a panel of clinicians and lay members. And in one hospital a professor of clinical ethics acts as a facilitator when teams are making the most difficult decisions, but does not take part in the actual decision; following the decision he helps staff to come to terms with the effects of that decision, if needed.

64. But such mechanisms are not always practical. Critical care doctors must make decisions more frequently and, sometimes, more quickly than these would allow. In such cases, making sure that genuine multidisciplinary team assessment takes place is important. In its latest report, the National Confidential Enquiry into Perioperative Deaths (NCEPOD) concludes that operations are taking place that are 'too adventurous, ill advised or futile, given the condition of the patient' (Ref. 48). NCEPOD recommends team assessment for, for example, all elderly surgical patients when contemplating radical surgery for malignant disease, because of the high incidence of other medical problems, and the limited benefit that surgery might bring in such cases. For patients likely to require critical care as a result of intervention, this should include input from unit staff because of their first-hand experience of likely survival and morbidity. Although greater clarity can be achieved by using such mechanisms, the point at which further treatment or resuscitation is no longer in the best interests of the patient will always be a judgement, and decisions will need to be taken on a case by case basis (Ref. 49).

65. In the case of persistent or permanent vegetative state (PVS), good practice guidelines have been issued that trusts could use as the basis for their own (Refs. 50, 51, 52 and 53). But there are other conditions where the same issues arise but for which no guidance exists. One clinical director at an inner-city hospital described admissions related to drug dependency. Whether a patient is admitted, despite the generally poor prognosis, depends partly on who is on duty at the time, the extent of their experience, and therefore the degree of confidence that they have in whether the patient is likely to survive. But the frequency of such cases has increased to the extent that clinical directors now feel that they must develop an explicit policy for these patients.

66. And a way should be found to explain in plain English what the trust's policies mean for the relatives of patients who are admitted – or not – to critical care units. The role of the trust board in these kinds of issues, in the light of the new clinical governance proposals, is taken up in the final chapter. This section also links to the next chapter, which begins by considering other ways in which pressure is put on critical care beds. Some of the quality improvements described above – for example, initiating follow-up clinics and rehabilitation programmes – cost money. However, the next chapter shows that there is scope for efficiency improvements in many units that would enable some of these improvements to be funded.

RECOMMENDATIONS

2 Improving Survival and Quality of Life

Highest priority recommendations	**Action needed by**
1 Improve the evidence base for critical care medicine by sponsoring multi-centre observational studies and, where it would not be unethical, randomised controlled trials into key interventions. Focus research on both survival and long-term effects on survivors.	NHS Executive NHS Directorate for Wales
2 Join the ICNARC programme, or a similar 'club' that allows comparisons of outcomes; using this information, review the clinical performance of general critical care units.	Chief executive Medical director Unit leaders
3 Find out relatives' views about their experiences in the unit via systematic satisfaction surveys.	Unit leaders

Medium priority recommendations	**Action needed by**
4 Focus clinical audit on key areas where clinicians differ in their preferred treatment approaches.	Unit leaders Medical director
5 Liaise with primary care and admitting consultants to provide rehabilitation services that meet the particular needs of ex-critical care patients, especially those who have been sedated for ventilation. If necessary, a specialist follow-up clinic service, and a rehabilitation programme, should be considered.	Unit leaders Admitting consultants GPs
6 Identify risks to consistency and continuity of care that are introduced by the consultant rota system and the way that nurses are allocated to patients; introduce mechanisms to minimise risks.	Unit leaders Director of nursing Medical director
7 Influenced by national guidance (recommendation 4, Chapter 4), develop an ethical policy, including general guidelines that: • state where patients in need of long-term or terminal care will be looked after; • place limits on treatment (for example, surgery) for patients with little hope of survival;	Chief executive Medical director Non-executive directors

RECOMMENDATIONS

- cover the conditions under which treatment should be withdrawn; and

- make explicit the status of advanced directives ('living wills') and 'do not resuscitate' orders.

8	Produce a booklet that explains the ethical policy for relatives in plain language.	Chief executive
	Basic recommendations	**Action needed by**
9	Develop a strategy that addresses the humanity of care and quality of life after discharge, in addition to survival.	Unit leaders
10	Pursue standardisation of intervention recording, for example, via a standard definition of the TISS system.	Intensive Care Society NHS Executive NHS Directorate for Wales
11	Clarify the current limitations of the method used by ICNARC and similar audit groups to adjust for casemix, and set target dates by which specific improvement will be achieved.	ICNARC Similar audit groups
12	Reinforce verbal information with plain language booklets for patients and relatives that explain:·	Unit leaders

- the way that the unit operates, location of facilities, and contact names; what to expect on arrival in the unit (for example, for major elective surgical patients);

- what to expect after discharge to the ward and from hospital; and

- the help available for bereaved relatives.

13	Review the accommodation available to relatives. As a minimum standard there should be, on or adjacent to the unit:	Unit leaders Director of quality

- a waiting room;

- a separate room where bad news can be given (apart from a cramped and busy sister's or doctor's office); and

- overnight accommodation.

RECOMMENDATIONS

14	Review provision for children against Paediatric Intensive Care Society guidelines; prepare a plan with target dates for feasible improvements; and a written policy on when children should be transferred to specialist facilities.	Unit leaders Director of quality
15	Review the service to bereaved relatives against the newly produced standards by the Intensive Care Society.	Unit leaders
16	Use a standard assessment procedure before discharge to identify those patients (and relatives) who are most likely to be in need of specialist rehabilitation due to their stay in critical care.	Unit leaders
17	Review staff communication systems (a questionnaire is available from local external auditors that can help identify problems).	Unit leaders Chief executive
18	Establish clear agreement between admitting and unit consultants about who is responsible for what (for example, initiating interventions, keeping relatives informed).	Unit leaders Clinical directors Medical director
19	Ensure that advice from consultants in the general ICU is available to, and made use of by, specialty-specific critical care units and, conversely, that specialty-specific advice is available to the general unit.	Unit leaders Clinical directors Medical director
20	Develop guidelines for common interventions to promote consistency of practice; audit compliance with guidelines.	Unit leaders
21	Agree a policy about the scope of nursing practice, describing the intended patient benefits and how it affects other disciplines; provide opportunities for training and a system for assessing competence; develop guidelines that set the parameters within which nurses can act autonomously.	Unit leaders Director of nursing

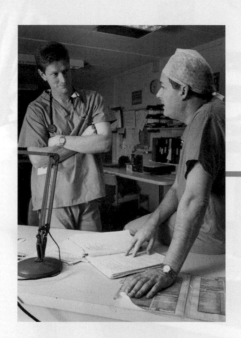

3

Reducing Costs through Flexibility

Improvements outside critical care units can reduce demand by preventing some patients from deteriorating into a need for critical care and by making sure that units do not contain patients who can be treated safely elsewhere. Efficiency improvements within units – both in bed management and the way that staff are deployed – can also reduce the cost of meeting patient needs. Some trusts face nurse shortages; the use of employee-friendly, flexible shift systems may help to relieve such shortages and to meet workload peaks and troughs economically.

67. There is a two-way interaction between critical care units and the rest of the hospital:

- *poor care or bed management outside units can unnecessarily inflate the demand for critical care beds:* for example, if wards fail to discharge patients promptly, then costly critical care beds can in turn be blocked with patients who do not need this level of care. On average, critical care units report delays equivalent to 5 per cent of occupied bed days, with a few trusts wasting substantially more [EXHIBIT 17A]; and

- *poor unit management can inflate costs and affect whole trust performance:* for example, if unit beds are full because some patients have been admitted unnecessarily or have not been discharged quickly enough, major surgery may be cancelled [EXHIBIT 17B]. On average, units report three cancelled operations for every 100 patients (both surgical and medical) whom they were able to admit, but a few trusts fare much worse. And higher critical care costs due to staffing inefficiencies or misuse of beds within the units can reduce resources available elsewhere in the hospital.

68. This chapter describes many ways in which costs can be controlled and efficiency improved, both outside and within critical care units. The key to most of them is a flexible approach to meeting variations in workload and good communications between unit staff and other departments. The chapter begins by examining how improving care outside critical care units can reduce pressures on unit beds. Next, it reviews whether unit beds are being used appropriately and efficiently. It then concentrates on the most expensive component of costs – the nurses who work on the units.

Improving care outside critical care units

69. Critical care units may become the backstop for a poorly performing hospital. Poor general care can result in patients needing critical care. This inflates the number of critical care beds required. Poor care may happen in A&E, the admissions unit, the operating theatre or on the wards [CASE STUDY 6, overleaf]. It can happen due to organisational failures, communication breakdowns, failure to seek consultant or specialist advice, failure to spot or act on danger signs, and failures in supervision and on-call response. Clinical directors and managers outside the units may not be aware that some of the causes of pressure on critical care units lie in their domain.

EXHIBIT 17A

Key examples of the two-way interaction of performance between critical care units and the whole trust

On average, critical care units report delays equivalent to 5 per cent of occupied bed days, due to a shortage of ward beds into which to discharge patients.

EXHIBIT 17B

Full unit beds can lead to major surgery being cancelled with, on average, three cancelled operations for every 100 patients (both surgical and medical) who are admitted.

Source: Audit Commission survey (115 and 108 units, England & Wales, 1997/98)

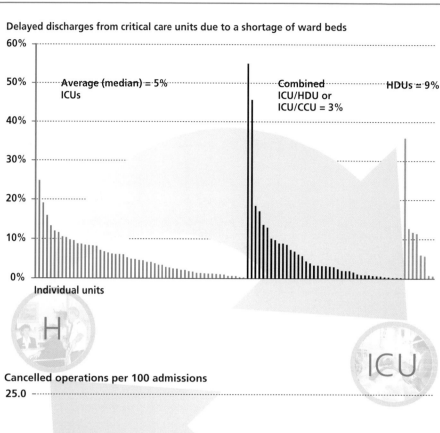

Delayed discharges from critical care units due to a shortage of ward beds

Average (median) = 5% ICUs — Combined ICU/HDU or ICU/CCU = 3% — HDUs = 9%

Individual units

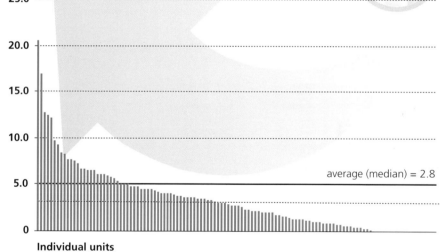

Cancelled operations per 100 admissions

average (median) = 2.8

Individual units

CASE STUDY 6

Patients deteriorating into a need for critical care due to failures in care management

Avoidable cardio-respiratory arrest

'Crash teams' resuscitate patients who have a cardiac arrest within the hospital. The number of patients can be significant in relation to the size of critical care units, where most such patients will subsequently go. A study of 47 cardiac arrests in one hospital [Ref. 54] found that over half the patients had shown a gradual deterioration with abnormal vital signs that would have allowed for intervention if the danger signs had been identified in time. But the study also identified some patients for whom intervention was inappropriate because they were too sick to benefit from either resuscitation or intensive care. 'Too often we see a haphazard trial of cardiopulmonary resuscitation followed by hasty referral to intensive care.' The authors recommend more proactive management for both sets of patients 'either to expedite referral for intensive care for those who need it or to allow a dignified death'.

Surgeon/anaesthetist management

Several critical care consultants reported that some surgeon/anaesthetist pairings managed patients in ways that are designed to avoid the need for admission to a critical care bed. One doctor gave the example of hip replacements – experienced surgeons were perceived to be less likely to need critical care facilities for their patients post-operatively than those who were new to it.

Source: Audit Commission interviews and Wood & Smith (Ref. 54)

70. In one study, intensive care doctors considered that half of the patients admitted from the wards had received inadequate care there. Most of them were admitted to the ICU late in their illnesses, and a substantial proportion of these admissions might have been avoided by better, more timely care on the wards (Refs. 55 and 56). A second study judged that nearly two out of every five admissions followed inadequate care (Ref. 57). Although the accuracy of professional judgement in estimating the numbers of patients affected has been questioned (Ref. 58), the principle – that better care could reduce admissions to critical care units – has not been challenged.

71. Some trusts have tried to improve ward staffs' recognition of the signs of deterioration. Examples include a centrally developed course for trainee surgeons (Ref. 59), and the training of ward nurses in recognition skills (Ref. 60). Such initiatives are often accompanied by well-publicised 'danger sign' guidelines that alert ward staff to the need to call either their consultant or a critical care doctor when physiological measures fall outside certain ranges (Refs. 61 and 62). This should be done in co-operation with the clinical directors of the surgical and medical specialties. At one

Better care could reduce admissions to critical care units

hospital visited, 'danger sign' guidelines, pinned on the wall by intensive care consultants, were taken down by one of the physicians because they had not been agreed for use.

72. The problem is not always just a lack of training. One trainee doctor described how the pre-registration surgical and medical house officers could have over 100 patients each to care for, so their time was spent reacting to problems that had already occurred, rather than seeking to prevent them (Ref. 63). In these circumstances it is the specialist registrars and consultants who need to oversee what is happening. A further step is for critical care doctors to take part in the care of some patients before admission to critical care units – a pre-admission triage or 'outreach' role [CASE STUDY 7].

CASE STUDY 7

Outreach from the critical care unit

'Patient at-risk team'

One hospital established a team that can be called to assess patients who show a combination of abnormal physiological measurements. A doctor or senior nurse can also call the team to patients who do not currently meet the criteria but who are causing concern. The team is made up of an intensive care doctor and nurse, the duty medical registrar and, for a surgical patient, the duty surgical registrar.

The physiological criteria are due for revision after audit showed that most patients to whom the team was called did not fulfil the main criteria. In six months the team was called to assess 63 patients, 60 per cent of whom were subsequently admitted to ICU. The team reports that awareness of potential patients on the wards allowed them to suggest changes in management, and also to plan ICU admissions.

Outreach by both doctors and a clinical nurse specialist

At one hospital visited, unit doctors and a clinical specialist nurse visit the wards on a daily basis to assess patients who may need admission, or to advise on treatment that can avoid admission. The unit has close links with A&E and is situated nearby, allowing joint management of patients before admission to the unit. The nurse specialist also helps in training ward staff how to care for patients with, for example, peripherally inserted central lines or epidurals, allowing such patients to be nursed on the wards rather than occupy critical care beds longer than necessary. This reflects the unit's aim to be an integral part of the hospital and not just where patients come for a brief life-saving episode.

Source: Goldhill et al. (Ref. 64) and Audit Commission site visit

73. In a half of all units, 14 per cent or more of admissions are pre-managed with the involvement of unit doctors. But in one-quarter of units the percentage is five or less.[I] Given that patients admitted from wards have, on average, the highest mortality [**EXHIBIT 18**], pre-involvement of critical care staff makes sense if early identification and intervention could reduce it. In particular, patients admitted from wards after cardiac arrest have very high mortality yet, as described above, some of these deaths should be preventable.

Managing patient flow

74. The previous section has shown that some of the patients in critical care units are there because of shortcomings outside the unit. But there is a further problem: patients who do not need the level of care provided may occupy beds. This section considers the difficulties involved in deciding who should be cared for in ICU, HDU or on a ward, and how long they should stay. It shows how trusts can achieve better value for money by managing the flow of patients between areas.

Placing patients appropriately

75. Chapter 2 ended by examining the ethical issues raised when patients are admitted who are too ill to benefit. Other patients may be too *well* to justify the higher staffing levels and expensive equipment. In one study of six hospitals, the admitting ICU doctors considered that 15 per cent of patients in their units were inappropriately admitted (Ref. 3). This is not an isolated example. Every study of patient placement reviewed by the Audit Commission has shown that critical care units contain such patients.

EXHIBIT 18

Mortality rates for patients admitted to ICUs from different sources

Patients admitted from the wards have, on average, the highest mortality.

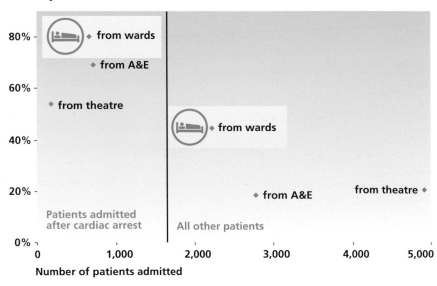

Mortality rate

Source: Audit Commission analyses of information from Goldhill & Sumner (Ref. 65) (15 units)

I   Source: ICNARC Case Mix Programme Database (79 units). The reliability of information returned from some of the outlying units with very high percentages is currently being examined, but is thought by ICNARC unlikely to affect the median value.

76. Department of Health guidelines (described below) suggest that most of the patients in an ICU should have more than one organ system in failure and that most patients will need ventilation during at least part of their stay. Because there are exceptions to these broad rules, exact figures about how many patients are misplaced cannot be calculated. But many of those units describing themselves as ICUs in fact contain large numbers of non-ventilated patients and those with only one organ system in failure [EXHIBIT 19].

77. Patients are wrongly placed for various reasons:

- *placement guidelines:* there are no admission and discharge guidelines in place, the guidelines are out of date or there is no system to check that they are being followed;

- *HDU:* there is no HDU, or the HDU's occupancy is kept up by placing patients there who in reality need only ward-level care; or

- *ward care:* wards do not provide the higher dependency care that some wards do in other hospitals.

78. The next few sections take each reason in turn and describe how the problems can be prevented.

EXHIBIT 19

The relationship between the percentage of patients within ICUs who were not ventilated at any point during their stay, and the percentage with only one organ system in failure

Department of Health guidelines suggest that most of the patients in an ICU should have more than one organ system in failure and that most patients will need ventilation during at least part of their stay. But many units in fact contain large numbers of non-ventilated patients and those with only one organ system in failure.*

*   Each point represents the averages for one unit.

Source: Audit Commission survey (47 units describing themselves as general ICUs, England & Wales, 1997/98)

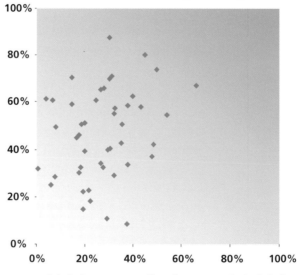

Admissions with fewer than two organs failing

Admissions not ventilated at any period of their stay

The further away a unit is from the bottom left corner, the more patients it contains who may not reach the Department of Health criteria for admission to an ICU

Trusts need to review their placement policies regularly to ensure that they are not out of date and causing higher costs rather than reducing inefficiency

Admission and discharge criteria

79. A substantial step forward in improving patient placement was the publication of guidelines in 1996 by the Department of Health, and Welsh Office guidance that expects each health authority and acute trust to agree detailed criteria. By 1998, three-quarters of units replying to the Audit Commission survey said that they had admission guidelines in place, and two-thirds had discharge guidelines. But guidelines are not always distributed. At one hospital visited, 21 of 23 referring consultants did not have copies. And they are not always followed – for example, making sure that a senior clinician is identified for each period of the day and night with responsibility for the 'gatekeeper' role is important.

80. Moreover, the Department of Health guidelines retain major areas where professional judgement is required. In a complex specialty, national guidelines must allow for local interpretation. But the risk is that substantial differences may appear between hospitals in their application. In particular, they leave the definition of which patients require high dependency care open to local interpretation and some hospitals choose to place a patient in their ICU that others would place in an HDU. This can double the nursing cost and prevent a bed being available to another patient. It makes sense for each trust to build on the general guidelines and define as far as possible specific interventions and patient types suited for intensive, high dependency or ward care, and to make sure that these definitions reflect a cost-effective use of higher staffing levels and expensive equipment. And because the boundaries of what is possible are changing all the time, trusts need to review their placement policies regularly to ensure that they are not out of date and causing higher costs rather than reducing inefficiency.

81. The Audit Commission has developed a survey tool, available to trusts, to help them to evaluate where patients are currently being placed in the hospital (Appendix 7). It is based on the Department of Health guidelines. Acknowledging that some degree of professional judgement is inevitable, the tool tries to make this explicit by recording objective information to help explain why patients have been deemed suited for ICU, HDU or ward placement. The results can help to stimulate debate and change within trusts, and ensure that expensive critical care beds are occupied by patients who really need them.

Use and mis-use of HDUs

82. Reducing the problem of improper use of ICUs has been one of the reasons for the creation of HDUs. Others include:

- offering a step up or step down bridge between an ICU and the level of care available on wards;

- reducing the number of patients who are refused admission or whose surgery is cancelled because other critical care beds are full; and

- ensuring that patients do not have to remain on a ward when it is considered unsafe.

83. These are key potential benefits, and it is understandable that critical care professionals often press for central HDU facilities. But their creation also introduces risks to value for money:

- high dependency beds can themselves become filled by patients who need only ward care. One study found that 53 per cent of HDU patients were appropriate for ward care [**CASE STUDY 8, overleaf**];

- patients moved via an HDU experience an extra movement of place, reducing continuity of care;

- some patients may receive a better quality of nursing care on a ward that specialises in particular conditions (for example, gastroenterology, renal failure) than in a general HDU; and

- the small size, with peaks and troughs of workload, can make it costly to staff the unit.

84. The keys to avoiding mis-use and realising the benefits of an HDU are the same as for ICUs – agreeing written admission and discharge guidelines, and making sure that they are properly applied and regularly reviewed. In addition, mis-use can be reduced if trusts pay close attention to the boundaries between what HDU and wards can do (next section) and form rotational links between ICU and HDU staff (Managing Staff Costs, below).

Higher-dependency care on wards

85. Complex treatments that would previously have taken place only in critical care units are now carried out in settings that may be cheaper and can relieve pressure on critical care beds. There may be other benefits, too. Wards contain more very sick patients as lengths of stay reduce and routine surgery is shifted to day surgery units. Attempting to keep the higher-dependency patients off the ward may be a fruitless battle against a rising tide that is better tackled by addressing nursing skills and staffing levels on the wards. Taking away the higher-dependency patients from wards also risks de-skilling and de-motivating ward nurses while, conversely, nursing them on wards provides empowerment and job satisfaction opportunities that may have important repercussions on ward nurse retention.

86. But hospitals vary considerably in how far they have developed higher dependency care in alternative settings. For example:

- a study across 26 hospitals found wide overlap in the interventions carried out on HDUs and wards. While some were rare on wards, other common HDU interventions, such as central venous pressure monitoring, also occurred on half of the wards (Ref. 67); and

CASE STUDY 8

Appropriate patient placement

In hospitals without an HDU, some patients with high-dependency needs are nursed either on the wards or expensively in an ICU (Example A). One solution is to create separate HDUs for these patients. However, some HDUs then in turn, offer poor value for money by admitting patients who do not reach the level of need for their services. In Example B, Over half of patients only needed ward care.

Key to shading	Clinically inappropriate?	Appropriate	Wasteful of resources

A. Eight hospitals *without* HDUs

Some patients on wards required high-dependency care, and patients not needing intensive care occupied half of the ICU beds.

Actual patient location	Patient need:		
	Intensive care	High-dependency care	Ward care
ICU	50%	50%	
Ward*		7%	70%

* The remaining 23 per cent of ward patients were judged as needing day or 'hotel' care.

B. Three hospitals *with* HDUs

Although the use of both ICU and ward beds is more appropriate, a new problem is introduced by inappropriate use of HDU beds. In these hospitals, most of the identified intensive care need was met, but HDU beds were greatly over-provided.

Actual patient location	Patient need:		
	Intensive care	High-dependency care	Ward care
ICU	98%	1%	1%
HDU	11%	36%	53%
Ward	<1%	<1%	>99%

Note: These tables have concentrated on the placements relevant to ICU, HDU or ward to emphasise what is especially relevant to a study of critical care. It is good practice, when conducting such a study, to further differentiate the ward category into, for example, patients suited to an inpatient ward or a day surgery unit, and patients suited to 'hotel' accommodation or long-term accommodation outside the acute hospital.

Source: Royal College of Anaesthetists & Royal College of Surgeons (Ref. 11) (A) and Donnelly et al (Ref. 66) (B)

- between one-quarter and one-third of hospitals incur extra costs and place unnecessary strain on critical care beds by nursing patients with epidurals for pain relief after major surgery within ICUs or HDUs [**EXHIBIT 20**]. Yet this treatment can be provided on wards because it does not require special equipment and is sufficiently common for ward nurses to take on. Safe provision on a ward requires training input, and the wards involved must be able to ensure that nurses with the required skills and time can be rostered for duty on a continuous basis, and that appropriate medical back-up is available. The training necessary for ward nurses will be easier to assure in hospitals where a clinical nurse specialist in pain control exists to support them (Ref. 68).

Ensuring high quality high dependency nursing care on wards

87. Trusts whose critical care beds are under severe pressure should review urgently the boundaries between which patients remain on wards and which enter an HDU [Appendix 5 gives further examples]. Ward staff cannot take on higher-dependency patients unless they are trained and supported [**CASE STUDY 9, overleaf**]. Such investment will enable the HDU to be used, as it should be, for patients with general system needs. For example, clinical audit results at one hospital visited found that 15 per cent of patients in the ICU were there because the ward nurses did not, in the judgement of the ICU staff, have the skills that were needed to care for the patients. A number of training schemes have now been described (Refs. 60 and 69). One trust visited has earmarked £1 million for ward nurse development and, in addition, has established a regular rotation system where surgical ward nurses rotate to the ICU for experience.

EXHIBIT 20

Where patients with epidural for pain control after major surgery are nursed

Between one-quarter and one-third of hospitals incur extra costs and place unnecessary strain on critical care beds by nursing patients with epidurals for pain relief after major surgery within ICUs or HDUs.

Source: Audit Commission (Ref. 68), 281 hospitals in the UK

Patients nursed

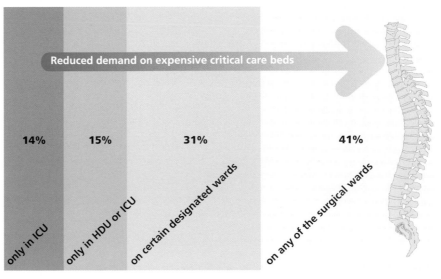

Reduced demand on expensive critical care beds

14% — only in ICU
15% — only in HDU or ICU
31% — on certain designated wards
41% — on any of the surgical wards

CASE STUDY 9

Wards differ in the type of high-dependency care that they can offer

Pre-operative testing to direct patient placement

In one hospital, pre-operative cardiopulmonary exercise testing is used to decide which high-risk surgical patients should be admitted after surgery to the ICU, HDU or ward [Ref. 70]. Since introducing the system, 25 per cent have been admitted to ICU, 25 per cent to HDU and 50 per cent to the ward. Only 2 out of 550 patients have subsequently needed to be moved to ICU from the ward. In addition to saving costs, the authors report reduced mortality and morbidity by more objective targeting of higher levels of care on those patients with objectively defined cardiovascular disease.

Overnight intensive recovery beds

Hospitals with large numbers of cardiac surgery patients can reduce pressure on general ICUs, and reduce cancelled surgery, by developing special overnight intensive recovery beds [Ref. 71].

Patients with aortic aneurysm

In most hospitals, patients operated on for aortic aneurysm will occupy an ICU bed. But in two hospitals visited, these patients now routinely go to the HDU after surgery, at lower cost and with a substantial reduction in bed pressures within the ICU. And a few hospitals with a large number of cases now keep such patients in recovery for two hours prior to going straight to a ward with staff who are trained in their care.

Patients suited to ward care will depend on ward nurse experience and training

At one hospital visited, a general medical ward with a gastrointestinal specialism nurses patients who are at risk of 'GI bleed' within the ward, rather than routinely transferring them to the HDU or ICU. Liaison with the crash team and the critical care units means that patients can be moved quickly from the ward if needed. On the other hand this ward, unlike some others, does not take patients with non-invasive breathing support (CPAP) in place because the nurses do not have sufficient experience to have developed the respiratory skills needed. If this ward has, for example, 33 'normal' patients and two high-dependency patients, then the most experienced nurses take responsibility for the latter. If necessary, bank nurses will be called in to help take care of other patients. The ward sister prefers not to transfer patients and relatives at a critical time when they have become familiar with their current ward. Transfers should happen only when there is a clear clinical need that overrides such concerns. It is important that ward nurses and medical staff know when to seek specialist advice.

Source: Older & Hall (Ref. 70), Aps (Ref. 71) and Audit Commission site visits

There is scope in some units to reduce lengths of stay

88. Increasingly reliable and portable monitoring equipment makes ward care possible for more dependent patients. Such systems can increasingly be routed through to a monitoring station, allowing critical care unit staff to give advice on changes in patients' status more readily. In addition, outreach links between critical care nurses and A&E, admissions units, recovery and the wards are likely to improve care outside the unit. While the majority do have links outside the unit, some say that they do not [TABLE 6].

Managing lengths of stay

89. The previous sections have shown how better demand management and patient placement could reduce costs. In addition, there is scope in some units to reduce lengths of stay. Casemix causes most of the variation in lengths of stay. But even when casemix is accounted for, units still differ. For example, the average length of stay for patients admitted with aortic aneurysm varies widely between units. This is still the case when only emergency patients are included. The longest lengths of stay are found in units that admit the fewest patients [EXHIBIT 21A, overleaf]. Although other casemix differences may still perhaps be involved, it may be that familiarity with the condition improves the efficiency with which cases can be managed.

90. Too short a length of stay in critical care is not cost-effective if patient outcome is poorer or re-admission is later needed. And timely admission of appropriate patients to an HDU may shorten overall hospital length of stay compared with trying to treat the patient on a busy ward where staff have not been properly trained and supported to provide the high-dependency care required. However, in the case of patients with aortic aneurysm, short lengths of stay in critical care are not followed by longer ward stays [EXHIBIT 21B, overleaf], suggesting that units achieving short lengths of stay do not do so by discharging patients too early.

TABLE 6

Critical care unit nurses visiting wards to offer outreach support and training

Percentage of units saying that this does occur	ICUs	ICU/HDU or ICU/CCU	HDUs
To offer specialist advice on particular patients	95%	96%	85%
To train ward staff in the care of high dependency patients	66%	62%	65%
Number of units	*116*	*101*	*34*

Source: Audit Commission survey (England & Wales, 1997/98)

EXHIBIT 21A

Length of stay for patients with aortic aneurysm

The longest lengths of stay for patients admitted with aortic aneurysm occur in units that admit fewest patients.

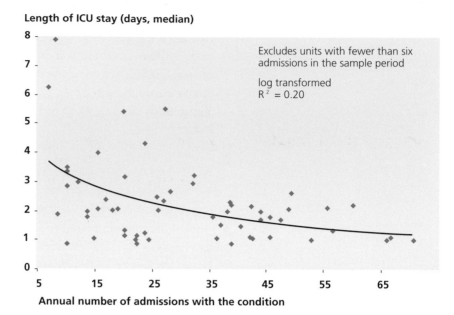

Length of ICU stay (days, median)

Excludes units with fewer than six admissions in the sample period

log transformed
$R^2 = 0.20$

Annual number of admissions with the condition

EXHIBIT 21B

Short lengths of stay are not followed by longer ward lengths of stay, suggesting that units achieving short lengths of stay do not do so by discharging patients too early.*

* In this and some of the following exhibits, the squared Pearson correlation coefficient is given. This estimates the amount of variation in one variable that can be explained by its relationship with another. In this case, the value $R^2=0.20$ estimates that 20 per cent of the variation in length of stay can be explained by the relationship with annual rate of admissions. Where the relationship is not linear, a transformation (in this case, log) has been applied to maximise the value of R^2.

Source: Audit Commission analyses of information from the ICNARC Case Mix Programme database (60 units)

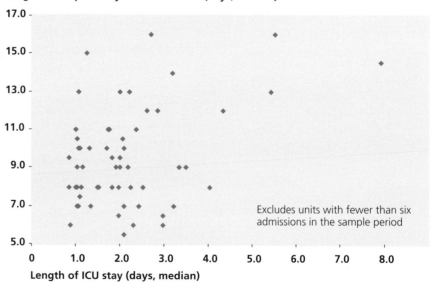

Length of hospital stay outside the ICU (days, median)

Excludes units with fewer than six admissions in the sample period

Length of ICU stay (days, median)

91. Units should carry out regular review of how they manage common conditions to identify any scope for safely reducing lengths of stay. Administrative systems can also affect lengths of stay. Good liaison between critical care unit and ward staff can ensure that lengths of stay are not inflated because of delays in organising discharge from critical care. While the majority of units (70 per cent) say that they visit wards to liaise over timings, this leaves a substantial number saying that this does not occur.

92. So far, this chapter has shown that both costs and the pressure on critical care beds can be reduced by concentrating closely on where patients are placed across the hospital, why they arrive in critical care units and how long they stay. Once these actions have been taken, trusts will be in a position to decide how many critical care beds are needed. This is a complicated process that must involve the trust board, and is discussed in Chapter 4.

Managing staff costs

93. Further opportunities for cost containment can be created by deploying staff more efficiently. Nurses account for 90 per cent of staff costs, and this section concentrates mainly on analysing the use of nursing resources.

Nurses

94. The general critical care units in England and Wales employ about 8,000 WTE nurses. They spend the majority of their time on direct patient care, mostly carrying out specific nursing and medical interventions (Appendix 6). The aim of managing a unit's nurses is to have the number and skill mix on duty that are needed by the patients at the least possible overall cost. Units vary considerably in how well they achieve this aim. For example, the 'average' unit has 5 direct care ('bedside') nurses on duty at any time. Some units employ twice as many nurses as others to provide them [EXHIBIT 22]. The same degree of variation is found in ICUs and HDUs.

95. The result of these differences in overall efficiency is a wide variation in the cost of nursing per patient day. For example, the top quarter of units describing themselves as ICUs are at least one-third more expensive than the bottom quarter, and some units at the extremes are twice as expensive as others [EXHIBIT 23, overleaf]. The reasons for these differences can

---

EXHIBIT 22

The relationship between the size of the nursing establishment* and the number of direct care nurses who are usually rostered for duty

Units vary greatly in establishment size and deployment efficiency.

*   Including senior unit nurses, temporary nursing staff and auxiliaries (healthcare assistants, etc), but excluding ward clerks. Here the mornings are used as an example, but the pattern is the same whichever period is chosen.

Source: Audit Commission survey (177 general ICUs, ICU/HDUs, ICU/CCUs and HDUs, England & Wales, 1997/98; excludes units that share establishments)

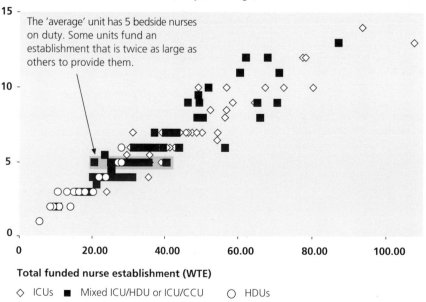

Usual number of bedside nurses on duty (mornings)

The 'average' unit has 5 bedside nurses on duty. Some units fund an establishment that is twice as large as others to provide them.

Total funded nurse establishment (WTE)

◇ ICUs   ■ Mixed ICU/HDU or ICU/CCU   ○ HDUs

EXHIBIT 23

The variation in critical care nursing costs per patient day

The cost of nursing per patient day varies greatly – for example, the top quarter of ICUs are at least one-third more expensive than the bottom quarter, and some units at the extremes are twice as expensive as others.

Source: Audit Commission survey (171 general ICUs, ICU/HDUs, ICU/CCUs and HDUs, England & Wales, 1997/98; excludes units that share establishments)

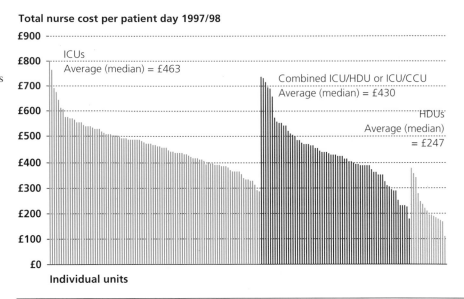

Total nurse cost per patient day 1997/98

ICUs
Average (median) = £463

Combined ICU/HDU or ICU/CCU
Average (median) = £430

HDUs
Average (median) = £247

Individual units

be understood only by breaking overall cost down into its different possible components. The rest of this chapter takes key examples and shows how the most economical units achieve their patient care aims.

Workloads – the number of patients and casemix

96. Nurse staffing levels should be determined primarily by workloads, the main component of which is the direct care given to patients (Appendix 6). Most units take casemix into account by aiming to have one bedside nurse for each intensive care patient (a 1:1 ratio) or for every two high dependency patients (1:2). Like most rules of thumb, this is not always appropriate. For example, a patient labelled as 'intensive care' who is stable and sedated may consume less nursing time than a 'high dependency' patient who is behaviourally disturbed. To overcome this variation, some units try to assess the dependency of each patient on a daily basis. Professional judgement is used to estimate the nursing needs, usually in increments of 0.5 of a whole-time equivalent (WTE) nurse. However, even where such systems are in place, units with the same workloads vary by at least 50 per cent in the number of nurses that they actually employ [EXHIBIT 24].

Staffing standards

97. Although the actual mix of patients does not explain differences in staffing levels, variation could be due to the casemix that managers *expect* to see on the unit in the coming year when they are deciding how many nurses to employ. The key standards that are applied when setting an establishment are the nurse:patient ratio required, the grade-mix and how many (if any) nurses will take no direct responsibility for the care of an individual patient. This section takes each of these factors in turn and then considers whether improvements to the process are possible.

EXHIBIT 24

The relationship between nurse staffing levels and patient workload

Units with average workloads differ greatly in nursing costs.

* The method weights each patient according to whether they have a low (weight = 0.5), medium (1.0), high (1.5) or very high (2.0) nursing dependency. It relies on the professional judgement of nurses when classifying patients.

Source: Audit Commission survey (74 general ICUs, ICU/HDUs, ICU/CCUs and HDUs, England & Wales, 1997/98)

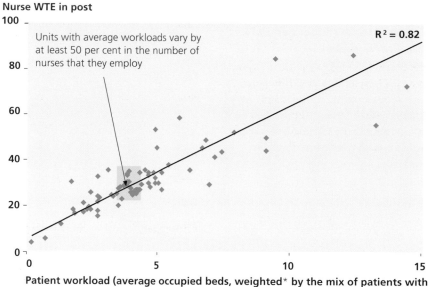

Nurse WTE in post

Units with average workloads vary by at least 50 per cent in the number of nurses that they employ

$R^2 = 0.82$

Patient workload (average occupied beds, weighted* by the mix of patients with differing nurse dependency)

Nurse:patient ratio

98. To achieve a ratio of 1:1 nursing in ICUs around the clock, the Intensive Care Society (ICS) recommends that units employ 6.3 WTE nurses per bed, or 7.0 WTE if 'the full complement of beds is to be maintained at all times' (Ref. 6). The average WTE employed per bed has risen from 5.2 in 1993 (Ref. 3), when the recommendation was to employ 5.5 WTE per bed, to 7.6 in 1998. However, there is considerable variation between units – for example, six-bedded ICUs (the average size) differ by 100 per cent in planned ('funded') staffing levels – and many units do not follow the ICS standards [**EXHIBIT 25, overleaf**].

Grade-mix

99. With its specialist and high-skilled nature, critical care is an area that requires a high proportion of nurses with post-basic training that is relevant to the area. Reflecting this requirement, the grade-mix tends to be richer – and therefore more expensive – than on general wards [**TABLE 7, overleaf**]. The main differences are:

- critical care units employ more E than D grade nurses, while wards employ more D than E; and

- critical care units employ fewer auxiliaries or healthcare assistants (in fact, nearly one-third of units do not employ any at all). In one unit visited, HCAs were assisting with direct care (for example, helping with dressings, tracheostomy care, turning, washing) and carried out many of the general functions for the whole unit (for example, stocking up store areas and trolleys, cleaning suction lines, washing and stripping ventilators down when patients are discharged).

Funded nurse WTE*

EXHIBIT 25

Funded nurse WTEs per general critical care unit bed, in relation to staffing standards

There is considerable variation between units – for example, six-bedded ICUs (the average size) differ by 100 per cent in planned ('funded') staffing levels – and many units do not follow the ICS standards.

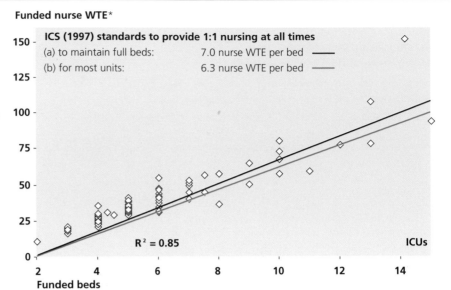

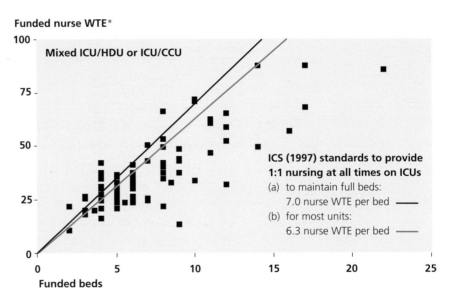

* Funded nurse WTEs are based on budgets and include senior nurses and auxiliaries or healthcare assistants (HCAs), but exclude ward clerks. 7 WTE per bed is described by the Intensive Care Society as the 'realistic' allocation to maintain a full complement of beds at all time. 6.3 WTE is the minimum stated allocation to provide 1:1 nursing and a nurse in charge or 'runner/floater'. The equivalent HDU lines are calculated from the standard that each patient needs half the number of nurses.

Source: Audit Commission survey (199 general ICUs, ICU/HDUs, ICU/CCUs and HDUs, England & Wales, 1997/98, excluding those that share establishments)

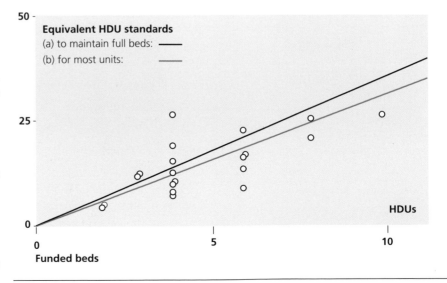

TABLE 7

The grade-mix* within critical care units compared with acute hospital wards

Nursing grade	ICUs	ICU/HDUs or ICU/CCUs	HDUs	Acute hospital wards
I	1%	<1%	<1%	–
H	2%	2%	1%	<1%
G	10%	10%	5%	4%
F	13%	13%	8%	6%
E	42%	40%	40%	23%
D	27%	29%	32%	32%
C	<1%	1%	1%	2%
Auxiliary, healthcare assistant	4%	5%	13%	32%
Number of units/wards	106	94	25	603

* Funded establishments (WTE)

Source: Audit Commission survey of critical care units (England & Wales, 1997/98) and District Audit surveys of general medical and surgical wards (England and Wales, 1996-98)

100. But there is no agreed method for determining what grade-mix is appropriate. There is no relationship between grade-mix richness in critical care units and the severity of illness of patients (as measured by APACHE II) or the proportion of patients with two or more organs in failure. Neither is there any overall tendency for units with higher-dependency patients to have a richer grade-mix. There is also no relation of grade-mix to staffing levels – units in general are not trading off grade-mix against 'numbers of hands'. This means that some units are parsimonious, and others expensive, in both levels and mix.

101. Grade-mix can also be affected by rules about the lowest grade of nurse that can take charge of a shift – two-thirds of units require an E grade, but one-third incur extra costs by stipulating an F grade or higher [EXHIBIT 26, overleaf]. No central standards have been issued about this, and there is no evidence about what effect differences might have on quality of care. Standards that cost more should be adopted only if this is a conscious decision, rather than one based on tradition. A quality benefit should be expected, and audit used to identify whether the benefits are subsequently achieved.

EXHIBIT 26

Lowest grade of nurse that can take charge of a shift

Two-thirds of units require an E grade, but one-third entail extra costs by requiring an F grade or higher to take charge.

Source: Audit Commission survey (240 general ICUs, ICU/HDUs, ICU/CCUs and HDUs, England & Wales, 1997/98)

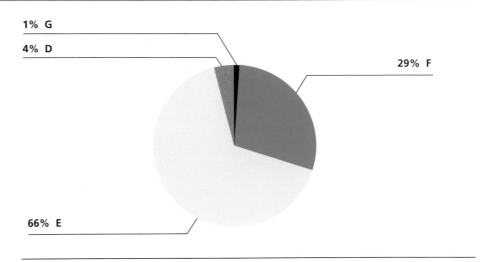

1% G

4% D

29% F

66% E

Non-bedside ('supernumerary') nurses

102. There are several kinds of nursing staff that may be deemed 'supernumerary' – that is, they are not allocated as the main care-giving nurse for individual patients, although they may assist in, observe, advise on or deliver some direct care during a shift. Units vary in such designations [TABLE 8] and few have any information about the effect of differences on the quality of patient care or staff satisfaction levels.

TABLE 8

The occurrence of 'non-bedside' nurses in critical care units

	ICUs	ICU/HDU or ICU/CCU	HDUs
Whether there are 'non-bedside' nurses (percentage of units answering 'yes'):			
Unit nurse manager or sister	53%	37%	26%
Shift leaders	32%	22%	6%
New recruits (for example, during an induction period)	78%	75%	59%
Nurses undergoing specialist training	41%	34%	26%
Units with no 'non-bedside' nurses of any of the above kinds (percentage)	22%	45%	64%
All 'non-bedside' nurses as a percentage of all nurse WTEs in post (median)	4%	2%	0%
Number of units/wards	*116*	*101*	*34*

Source: Audit Commission survey (England & Wales, 1997/98)

103. 'Non-bedside' nurses can make up a substantial percentage of the nurses on duty, especially in smaller units [**EXHIBIT 27**]. For example, one-third of ICUs designate their shift leader as 'non-bedside' [**TABLE 8**]. On average, such units will be about 20 per cent more expensive than those where the shift leader function is taken on by one of the bedside nurses. Economy of scale is involved – in a unit with only four beds, a 'non-bedside' shift leader represents a 25 per cent overhead cost on each bed, while in a 10-bedded unit, it is reduced to 10 per cent. One unit visited off-set this extra cost partly by giving the 'non-bedside' sister of a small HDU an additional clinical specialist role. She visits wards regularly to assess patients who may need admission, provides advice and training on high-dependency care for ward staff, and provides extra support for patients and relatives who have recently been discharged from the HDU. But, in most units, decisions about 'non-bedside' nurses are arbitrary.

Recruitment, retention, absence and cover

104. Some trusts report a shortage of intensive care nurses, especially those trained to ENB100 standard (specialist training in intensive care nursing) or the Welsh equivalent. Because the number of critical care nursing posts is growing, some units will have to take nurses without experience and provide training themselves. And they must compete with other specialties, since the growth in demand for critical care nurses is occurring at a time when new entrants to the general register of nurses from training has been declining faster than for many years (Ref. 72).

EXHIBIT 27

The relationship between the percentage of 'non-bedside' nurses and unit size (the number of nurses usually on duty)

The proportion of 'non-bedside' nurses can have a substantial impact on costs, especially in smaller units.

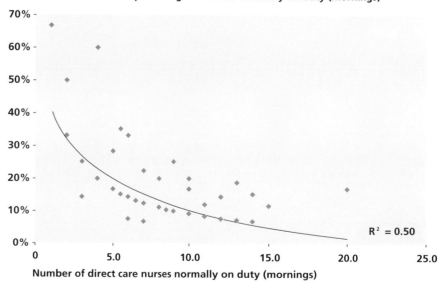

'Non-bedside' nurses as a percentage of nurses normally on duty (mornings)

$R^2 = 0.50$

Number of direct care nurses normally on duty (mornings)

Note: Excludes units that do not have 'non-bedside' nurses.

Source: Audit Commission survey (117 general ICUs, ICU/HDUs, ICU/CCUs and HDUs, England & Wales, 1997/98)

NATIONAL REPORT • CRITICAL TO SUCCESS

105. Recruitment problems will be exacerbated by turnover, which varies considerably between units [EXHIBIT 28]. The costs of turnover have been estimated at £5,000 per qualified nurse that leaves the NHS (Ref. 73). The bulk of this figure is taken up by the cost of inducting and training new staff, with the remainder by the cost of temporary cover and the recruitment process itself. Using this figure, the annual cost of turnover in critical care units for the average-sized trust is £14,000 – the equivalent of about one grade D nurse's salary. Across all units, the annual cost of turnover, based on this estimate, is about £5.5 million, equivalent to 3 per cent of the 1997/98 critical care nursing wage bill in England and Wales.

106. The most serious problems are in big cities, especially London, and in some of the more remote rural locations [EXHIBIT 29]. Recruitment difficulties were the most common main reason for vacancies (cited by 43 per cent of units), with the other reasons including a conscious decision to alter the grade-mix (16 per cent) and the requirement by the trust to carry a vacancy factor (5 per cent). Those units that stated that vacancies were mainly due to recruitment difficulties had vacancy levels that were on average five times higher than the rest (10 per cent as against 2 per cent). The majority of trusts with recruitment problems have vacancies at both D and E grades, especially the latter who are usually required to have the ENB 100 qualification.

EXHIBIT 28

Variation in the rates at which nurses leave critical care units

Staff turnover varies considerably between units.*

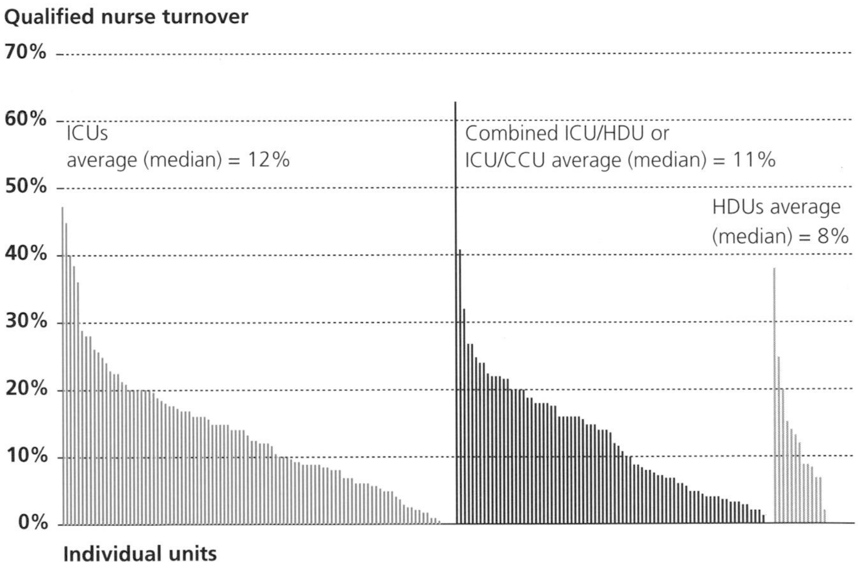

* The number of nurses who left to join another critical care unit, or who were 'lost' to the specialty in the short or long-term, is unknown.

Source Audit Commission survey (202 units, England & Wales, 1997/98)

Qualified nurse turnover

ICUs average (median) = 12%

Combined ICU/HDU or ICU/CCU average (median) = 11%

HDUs average (median) = 8%

Individual units

EXHIBIT 29

Geographical variation in nurse vacancy rates

There is a marked geographical pattern to vacancy rates – the most serious problems are in big cities, especially London, and in some of the more remote rural locations.*

* The size of each dot is exactly proportional to the percentage of vacancies, ranging in size from no vacancies (the smallest dots) to 53 per cent vacancies (the unit with the largest dot).

Source: Audit Commission survey (230 general ICUs, ICU/HDUs, ICU/CCUs and HDUs, England & Wales, 1997/98)

107. In addition to finding cover for vacant posts, some trusts must find cover for a higher than average level of sickness absence (the average, from survey returns, is 4 per cent annually). One way is to pay for more temporary nurses to cover; another is to employ more establishment nurses per bed to compensate for high expected absence; or to keep some beds closed. On average, the costs of providing temporary cover amounts to 4 per cent of total expenditure on nurses [EXHIBIT 30]. Units can either pay their own nurses overtime, bring in their own staff from an internal bank (similar to paid overtime but usually at normal rather than enhanced overtime rates) or hire nurses from an agency. The use of agency nurses is patchy – nearly half of units did not employ them during 1997/98, but other units rely heavily on them to keep beds open. And for a handful of units, they represent more than one-third of total nurse costs.

Flexibility: the most important reason for nurse cost differences

108. This section on nurse staffing has shown that there are many reasons for cost variation and that units are susceptible to different problems. Multivariate analyses do not reveal any combination of factors that can systematically explain the differences in the cost of nursing between units. However, if the 15 cheapest and most expensive general ICUs are compared, one of the main reasons for high nursing costs is that some units deploy a nurse to each bed even if it is empty or occupied by a high-dependency patient. The economical units are significantly more likely to use flexible shift arrangements to stand staff down if occupancy and dependency are low. In addition, these units are significantly less likely to have 'non-bedside' shift leaders [TABLE 9].

EXHIBIT 30

Expenditure by critical care units on temporary nursing staff*

On average, the costs of providing temporary cover amounts to 4 per cent of total expenditure on nurses. Some units favour using their own staff, others agencies, and others a mixture of the two.

* Bank, agency and paid overtime.

Source: Audit Commission survey, (223 general ICUs, ICU/HDUs, ICU/CCUs and HDUs, England & Wales, 1997/98)

The cost of temporary nursing staff as a percentage of total nurse expenditure

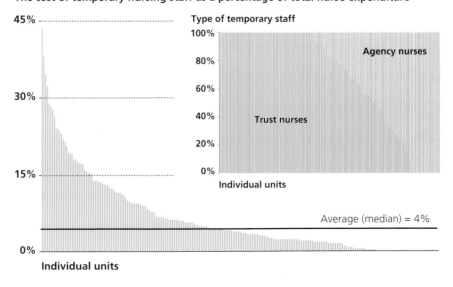

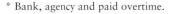

TABLE 9

Flexible nurse staffing mechanisms and nurse staffing cost differences between ICUs

	The 15 cheapest ICUs	*All 116 ICUs*	The 15 most costly ICUs
Averages for the 15 ICUs with the highest nurse cost per patient day and the 15 with the lowest cost:			
Average funded nurse whole time equivalents (WTEs) per bed*	5.3	*5.8*	8.1
Percentage of units making use of each mechanism:			
Flexible shift start or finish times*	47%	*42%*	20%
Standing staff down if occupancy is low*	53%	*44%*	21%
Standing staff down if dependency is low*	40%	*28%*	7%
Shift leader is 'non-bedside'*	8%	*32%*	42%
Other flexible mechanisms with no significant difference in use between the cheapest and most costly units:			
Annualised hours contracts		*8%*	
Hiring extra staff to temporarily open beds		*48%*	
Paying the trust's own nurses overtime or bank hours to open beds		*84%*	

* Variables where the cheapest and most costly ICUs differ significantly (1- tailed T-tests; $p < 0.05$).
The cheapest units had, on average, fewer ventilated patients (63 per cent compared with 79 per cent) but did not differ significantly in other measures of workload – for example, patient dependency or the proportion of high-dependency days. The cheapest and most expensive groups both contain, on average, six beds – the same as the average for all ICUs. The two groups did not differ in casemix-adjusted mortality.

Source: Audit Commission survey (England & Wales, 1997/98)

109. A flexible approach becomes the key to achieving a high level of service while containing staff costs [EXHIBIT 31]. Units should deploy staff according to the true mix of intensive care and high-dependency patients that the unit admits, and not simply staff all beds at 1:1 just because the unit is called an 'ICU'. The most successful of these units are valued by nurses since the use of variable shift systems to meet service aims may also help to meet the demands of family life. Staffing arrangements should be agreed that allow nurses to be stood up or down as patient needs vary, coupled with shift systems with variable start and finish times that can be altered to match patient needs [CASE STUDY 10]. An element of choice is crucial: whether a nurse wants to work short shifts with variable start and finish times will depend on personal circumstances.

EXHIBIT 31

Key influences on the cost of critical care nursing per patient day

A flexible approach becomes the key to achieving a high level of service while containing staff costs.

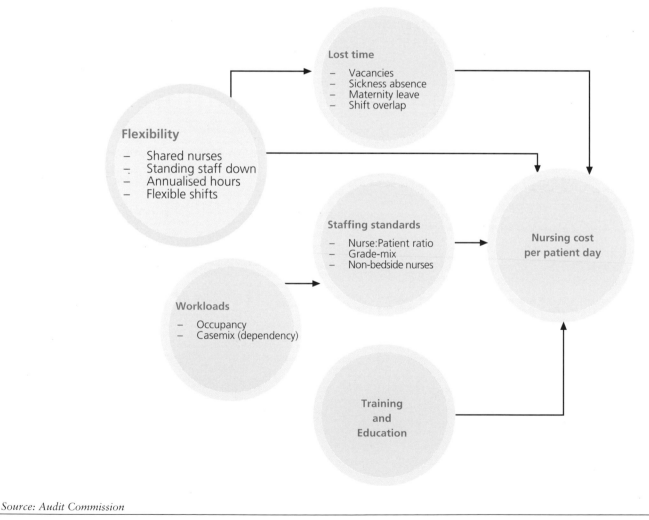

Source: Audit Commission

CASE STUDY 10

Employee-friendly, flexible working arrangements

One establishment for several units

One hospital has a single nursing establishment for intensive and high dependency care, coronary care and the acute assessment/admissions unit. Nurses rotate through the different areas, build up expertise in each and can be deployed flexibly to match workloads.

Flexible use of beds and staff for intensive, high dependency or coronary care

This hospital has 14 critical care beds that are designated as five ICU, three HDU and six CCU. However, they can be used interchangeably to match demand. The beds are located in two geographically separate units but are staffed and run as one. Nurses rotate between the units on a regular basis, and can be deployed shift-by-shift depending on the workload and level of dependency.

Fixed and variable elements of the establishment

In this large unit, the annual budget is based on a fixed element, at 5.3 WTE per bed, which covers the usual occupancy of 70 per cent. Most occupancy above that consists of patients who attract extra-contractual referral payments, which is used to fund the variable aspect of the establishment. These nurses are called in flexibly to match the extra workloads – preferably via the bank but, given the big city location, the unit also has to use agency nurses at times.

Annualised hours hospital

An annualised hours system operates in a number of areas within the hospital, including the ICU. Nurses are contracted to work a number of hours in a year rather than a number of hours per week – the contract is for 1,957 hours in a year (equivalent to 37.5 hours X 52.18 weeks) which, after holiday and training allowances, is reduced to 1,670 hours work. They receive a standard monthly salary irrespective of the actual hours worked, and thus can be called in during periods of peak demand, and work fewer hours when demand is low. This is reported to offer similar levels of stability to a normal system, because the conventional duty rosters were often subject to change anyway. In addition to better matching of staff to workload variations, the trust reports reduced use of bank staff and reduced overall labour costs. Staff benefits are perceived to be financial security, a more stable training and development environment as dependence on temporary staff reduces, and flexible working patterns.

Other arrangements

In addition to variable shift systems, other mechanisms described by unit managers include informal last minute swapping of shifts between colleagues – for example, in response to an illness in one family. Some vary the number of working hours in the different weeks across the four-week period over which the off-duty is usually planned. These systems rely on co–operation between colleagues.

Source: Audit Commission survey and Spoerry [Ref. 74]

110. Where an HDU exists, integrated ICU/HDU nurse establishments offer the potential to make more efficient use of staff, with cost savings. However, such sharing of staff is relatively rare [TABLE 10]. But there are pros and cons to integration that need to be considered before a trust decides whether, in its particular circumstances, integration is the best approach [BOX C]. Other options are to rotate staff through A&E, theatre recovery and specialist critical care units elsewhere in the hospital.

111. The mechanisms just described can be used now. In the longer-term, more fundamental change may be possible. If the tendency to expand the scope of nursing practice continues (Chapter 2), making qualified nurses more comprehensive carers, then a case begins to emerge for changing the way that they offer direct care, especially when nurses with these higher skills are in relatively short supply. One senior nurse interviewed thought the future lay in having a lower-graded nurse allocated to each individual patient, and a higher-graded, higher-trained and very experienced nurse responsible for the care planning and prescription for several of these nurses and patients. This may be easier to introduce first in single-specialty units where the types of patients are similar and skills can be more quickly learnt and regularly applied [CASE STUDY 11, overleaf].

TABLE 10

Mechanisms for sharing nurses between critical care units

Percentage of units answering 'yes'	ICUs	ICU/HDU or ICU/CCU	HDUs
The nurse establishment for two or more units is integrated	11%	4%	24%
Nurses may temporarily work in other units or on wards	43%	33%	54%
Number of units	*103*	*91*	*24*

Source: Audit Commission survey (England & Wales, 1997/98)

BOX C

Separate or mixed ICU and HDU?

Some trusts integrate their ICU and HDU. Integration can be geographical, in that beds are interchangeable within the same unit or in adjacent areas. Or it can mean sharing staff or treating them as a single establishment. Wherever possible, equipment and staff should be moved to the patient and not the other way round. A shared establishment makes economic sense, is likely to improve continuity of care for patients and reduces the anxieties associated with moving from one environment to another.

Pros	Cons
Separate units	
Protected step-down bed availability	No extra flexible intensive care capacity
Patients and relatives with lesser illnesses are not mixed with very anxious or bereaved relatives of intensive care patients	Less continuity of care for patients, and the anxiety of moving to a new and unfamiliar environment
Mixed units	
If a patient has a crisis on the HDU, ICU doctors and nurses are nearby to help out	
Cost-efficiency for staffing, less duplication of equipment	In times of bed stress, high dependency beds are lost because they are used for intensive care
A larger pool of nurses with specialist qualifications and experience to draw on	Some nurses may have less experience in either intensive care or high dependency
Some nurses enjoy the variety and opportunity for a less stressful 'break' by caring for both intensive care and high dependency patients	Some nurses prefer the type of work and atmosphere found in HDUs, or vice-versa, in ICUs

Source: Audit Commission

CASE STUDY 11

A development forward from the basic 1:1 nurse:patient concept

One cardiothoracic unit has instigated a team-nursing system where an F or G grade nurse manages more than one patient in partnership with specially trained 'intensive care assistants' (ICAs). How many patients a team takes responsibility for on a shift depends on their needs, as judged by the shift leader. For example, a pairing of a qualified nurse and an ICA might take one ventilated patient and one less dependent patient between them.

The ICA is trained to NVQ level 2, and has more specialised skills than most HCAs. The training allows, for example, the ICA to run a blood sample through the blood gas analysis machine and bring the results back, meaning that the qualified nurse does not have to leave the patient's bedside. In this system, the ICAs are seen as integral members of one of the nursing teams, rather than as a general resource for the whole unit.

The nurses involved believe that quality has improved since the system was implemented, nurses' job satisfaction has increased and stress reduced. It means that the unit is able to satisfy trust demands for more patients to be treated, while reducing unit costs per bed and avoiding problems of the short supply of qualified nurses.

Source: Roberts & Cleary (Ref. 75)

112. However desirable it is that units should be able to identify the number of staff needed in their establishments more accurately, the many variables involved (Appendix 6) make it clear that a simple formula is not the main answer. Nationally sponsored research should take place to record more scientifically the cost-benefits offered by 1:1 nursing, and establish whether it really matches what patients and relatives need. The Department of Health, while recommending the use of 1:1 at the moment, has nevertheless also called for research into a more precise method (Ref. 76). This should be forward-looking, taking into account the changing scope of nursing practice described in Chapter 2 and the notion of team-based nursing described in Case Study 11.

Doctors

113. In an area where multidisciplinary teamworking is of particular importance, the numbers and skill mixes of the different staff groups should be jointly planned. Although this happens in some trusts, there is no evidence that it does in the majority. Units that employ a large nursing workforce do not necessarily employ high numbers of other staff to meet higher workloads. Nor, on the other hand, do they trade off expenditure on nurses by making do with fewer doctors, as might be expected if one group were substituting for another. And there is no overall tendency for trusts to balance a low grade-mix of one group of staff with higher mix in another. For example, units with only less experienced trainee doctors

(SHOs) and no specialist registrars (SpRs) do not have a higher nursing grade-mix or higher standards about the grade of nursing shift leaders (in fact, the opposite is the case).

114. One aspect of this varied pattern is that similar-sized ICUs differ by 300 per cent in consultant costs – for example, some trusts fund five notional half days (NHDs) or sessions, and others 20 or more to cover an average-sized, six-bedded unit [**EXHIBIT 32**]. All ICUs, 95 per cent of mixed units and half of HDUs have some designated consultant cover, with 93 per cent of such sessions assigned to doctors with the parent specialty of anaesthesia. Of the remaining sessions, half are assigned to those with a background in general medicine and the remainder to a wide range of other specialisms (including cardiology, paediatrics and a variety of surgical specialties).

115. Currently:

- 23 per cent of ICUs meet the Association of Anaesthetists' recommendation of 15 consultant sessions (ten for normal hours cover and five for out of hours) (Ref. 2);

- 46 per cent meet the minimum standard of the Intensive Care Society for all ten Monday-Friday mornings and afternoons to be covered by a consultant (Ref. 6); and

- 76 per cent meet the Intercollegiate Board standard of at least seven sessions covered (Ref. 77).

EXHIBIT 32

Consultant sessions and unit size

Similar-sized ICUs differ greatly in consultant costs.

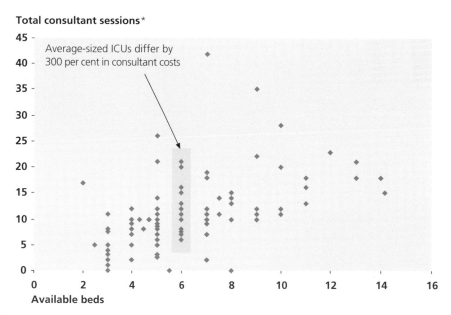

Total consultant sessions*

Average-sized ICUs differ by 300 per cent in consultant costs

Available beds

* Normal hours and, where specifically identified by trusts, at other times.

Source: Audit Commission (111 general ICUs, England & Wales, 1997/98)

116. The number of consultant sessions is growing quickly – 40 per cent of units said that they expected the number of designated sessions to grow in the next financial year, on average by three NHDs. But the number of different standards which units may aim for could lead to confusion. Cross-trust research is needed to establish guidelines that are related to the size and workload of units.

Opportunities for cost reduction

117. This chapter has identified many different cost components. Trusts can use the comparative information to identify targets for priority action in their particular circumstances. Some improvements will be harder to achieve than others – for example, changing care management to reduce lengths of stay safely may be more difficult to achieve than ensuring that a senior clinician acts as admission 'gatekeeper' on each shift. It will also be difficult to reduce the number of patients who deteriorate on the ward, if long-term improvements in training are needed. But, in the short-term, a degree of advance warning when a patient is deteriorating is possible if there is good liaison, and this can make efficient use of units more achievable. Many of the improvements share this need for good communications and a flexible response. The role of the trust board in improving communications, efficiency and outcomes is the key theme of the next chapter.

RECOMMENDATIONS

3   Reducing Costs through Flexibility

	Highest priority recommendations	**Action needed by**
1	Improve services for patients on wards who are at risk of deteriorating into a need for critical care:	Medical director Clinical directors Unit leaders

- review trainee doctor and senior ward nurse recognition skills of the early warning signs;
- agree 'danger sign' guidelines to help ward staff to identify when to call for specialist advice to prevent deterioration; and
- develop an 'outreach' service from critical care specialists to support ward staff in managing patients at risk.

2	Conduct regular audit to identify the number of unit beds that are occupied by patients who cannot benefit because they:	Unit leaders Medical director

- are too ill and cannot recover;·
- could be cared for safely elsewhere – for example, in an HDU not an ICU, or in a ward rather than an HDU; and
- remain in the unit only because ward beds are blocked and unavailable to discharge patients into.

3	Set annual nurse staffing budgets at ratios that match the expected mix of intensive and high-dependency care patients in the unit, not at a rigid 1:1 nurse:patient ratio just because the unit is labelled 'the ICU'. On a daily basis, deploy nurses to match the actual number and dependency needs of patients in the unit, not at a ratio of one nurse to one bed irrespective of whether the bed is occupied.	Director of finance Unit leaders

	Medium-priority recommendations	**Action needed by**
4	Review where 'borderline' patients are currently placed. Invest in ward skills, equipment and staffing levels where this is more cost-effective than placing such patients in expensive critical care units.	Unit leaders Medical director Director of nursing Clinical directors
5	Sponsor cross-trust research to establish new guidelines for estimating consultant staffing levels that take account of unit size and workloads.	NHS Executive NHS Directorate for Wales Intensive Care Society

RECOMMENDATIONS

6   Review the percentage of costs accounted for by non-bedside ('supernumerary') nurses, in relation to the benefits that they are expected to provide.

Unit leaders

7   Sponsor cross-trust research to establish new, more objective guidelines for estimating nurse staffing levels that take account of changing nursing roles, including changes to the scope of practice.

NHS Executive
NHS Directorate for Wales
BACCN
RCN Critical Care Forum

8   Introduce flexible, employee-friendly ways to match nurses to patient needs and to ease recruitment and retention problems (for example, flexible shifts, annualised hours contracts, standing staff down when occupancy and dependency are low).

Unit leaders

Basic recommendations

Action needed by

9   Review the scope for other cost-effective alternatives to critical care units – for example, overnight intensive recovery beds for large-volume cardiac hospitals.

Medical director
Clinical directors

10   Following that review:·

- agree guidelines for admission to and discharge from critical care units, based on those published by the Department of Health, but incorporating specific rules about areas that the national guidelines leave to local choice; and

- update the guidelines periodically, because what can safely be provided on the wards changes with improved technology and training.

Unit leaders
Medical director
Clinical directors
Director of nursing

11   Conduct regular audit to identify the number of unit beds that are occupied because of:

- failure to spot abnormal signs on the wards leading to avoidable deterioration into a need for critical care;

- surgery or other treatment for patients that do not benefit; and

- inadequate surgical or anaesthetic management.

Unit leaders
Medical director
Clinical directors

RECOMMENDATIONS

12 Check unit lengths of stay to ensure that clinical management is not leading to longer stays than can safely be achieved in other units and that stays are not extended because of poor liaison over discharge arrangements.

Unit leaders
Clinical directors
Director of nursing

13 Compare doctor and nurse staffing costs with similar trusts using data and software provided by local auditors appointed by the Audit Commission.

Chief executive
Unit leaders

14 Review the potential for healthcare assistants or nursing support workers to reduce qualified nurse time spent on activities that do not make good use of their time.

Unit leaders

15 Review the cost-effectiveness of shift systems and overlaps.

Unit leaders

16 Review the pros and cons of integrating separate ICUs and HDUs to maximise flexible options for matching nurses to patient needs and reducing overall costs.

Medical director
Director of nursing
Unit leaders
Clinical directors

4———

Managing a Complex Network

The trust board needs to plan the configuration of critical care units carefully. It must foster good communications across clinical directorates to ensure that the network of critical care services meets the trust's needs. To meet clinical governance requirements, the board needs to put in place an information and audit system so that it can review casemix-adjusted performance.

118. Previous chapters show that critical care services are complex, and the quality and the efficiency with which they are delivered are inextricably linked to what happens elsewhere in the hospital. Some challenges cannot be solved solely by critical care staff. This chapter explains how board involvement can set the framework for a better use of resources, improving the trust's performance as a whole. It concentrates on two key aspects of the board's involvement: assessing need and planning the configuration of services across the trust, and in clinical governance.

Why the trust board should be involved

119. There has been no national plan for adult intensive care services. And, since the cessation of the regional health authorities, there has also been only limited regional planning of service configuration. This lack of central planning is often repeated at the level of the acute trust. But the trust board should be involved [BOX D, overleaf].

Service planning

120. Given the demand pressures described in the Introduction, many trusts will be reviewing the number of ICU beds that they currently provide. Trusts should not carry out such reviews in isolation. General ICUs are part of a network of acute hospital care, along with specialist critical care units (for example, those for renal care, burns, neurosurgery, coronary care and children), general high-dependency units (HDUs), A&E, admissions units, recovery and the wards [EXHIBIT 33, overleaf]. Trusts will need to map the current configuration of units, and the flow of patients both between them and other areas of the hospital, building on the information described in Chapter 1. Examining this process in detail is beyond the scope of this report. But this section gives guidance on how to assess the need for critical care beds within the context of a whole-hospital review.

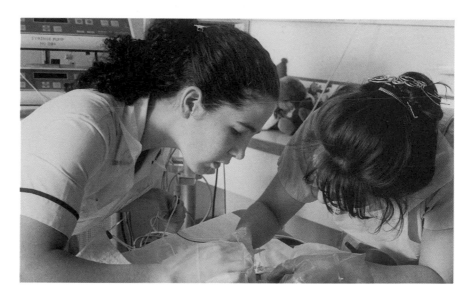

BOX D

The trust board's role in critical care services

The trust board needs to set the framework for better use of critical care and other services to improve the trust's performance as a whole. It needs to assure itself that the following are in place:

Unit management

- ensure that critical care units are well-managed (the same principles apply to critical care units as to other areas – general principles for anaesthesia departments have been listed in a previous Audit Commission report [Ref. 68], while Chapters 2 and 3 contain specific recommendations for critical care unit managers);

Configuration of services

- assess the number of patients within the hospital who require intensive and high dependency care and debate the configuration of units, A&E, admissions unit and ward care that will best meet these needs;

- decide on the best mix of general and specialist units, bearing in mind the trade-offs between quality, ring-fencing of beds, costs and ease of transfer between the units;

- set the quality standards that the trust wishes to achieve;

Communications

- co-ordinate development of agreed guidelines on the transfer of patients between units and wards in different directorates, to make sure that the whole resource is used efficiently and that continuity of patient care is protected;

- foster good communications between clinical directorates to ensure efficient use of the total resource;

- identify who should have the day-to-day powers to make decisions that follow the guidelines and ensure that the decisions are implemented, and make it clear within the hospital who these people are;

- make sure that training arrangements are adequate both to prevent patients from deteriorating into a need for critical care across the hospital, and to enable care of some higher-dependency patients to take place when appropriate on the wards;

Ethics

- develop, with clinicians, ethical policy on who should or should not enter critical care units, and when they should be discharged;

- tackle any controversial treatments outside units that place extra demands on over-stretched critical care beds, but over which intensive care staff have no control;

- set in place processes to ensure the policy is followed (for example, admission and discharge guidelines that include ethical decision-making; a committee that will review rare, difficult, cases);

- make it known that, when time and circumstances allow, it wants teams rather than individuals to take difficult ethical decisions and, therefore, it promotes ways of multidisciplinary communication and case conferencing;

- support clinicians in making difficult and stressful decisions, without interfering in individual decisions;

- review audit results to ensure that critical care units are being used in accordance with the strategic framework that they have set, and are delivering the quality level to which the trust aspires; and

- put in place a management structure, information system and audit framework that can allow the developments listed above to happen.

Source: Audit Commission

EXHIBIT 33

Critical care as part of the network of care delivered by an acute hospital

Critical care forms an essential part of a network of care that makes up an acute hospital.

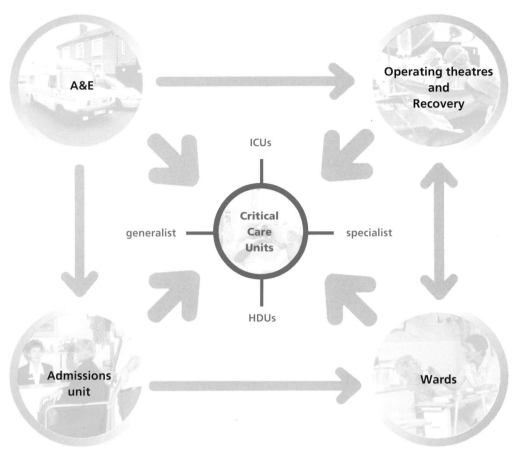

Source: Audit Commission

121. Given what is known about the history of directorate development and relationships across the hospital, trusts need to consider how likely it is that this whole network of critical care resources is being well used. Differences of opinion and judgement are likely and will affect how well the whole resource is used, and the board will need to clarify these, involving working doctors and nurses in their discussions. And, as described in Chapter 3, trusts must also make sure that they are managing demand and using current beds appropriately and efficiently, before considering supply-side increases [EXHIBIT 34, overleaf]. This means both improving care on ordinary wards and the management of critical care units to reduce the unnecessary spiralling of costs and pressures. The hallmarks of trusts that do not do this contrast with those that reduce bed pressures by planning [BOX E, overleaf].

EXHIBIT 34

Breaking the upward spiral of critical care costs

Critical care services are under pressure, and there are no simple, quick fixes. The solution lies in managing the demand for critical care beds as well as their supply.

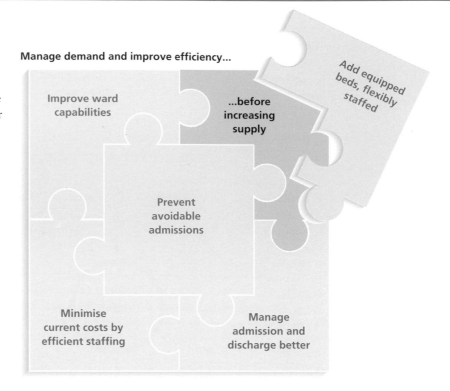

Source: Audit Commission

122. There are no simple, quick fixes. Many patients have complicated histories, are already receiving multiple drug regimens and are in multi-system failure. The likely outcome of treatment alternatives is rarely clear cut, and sometimes difficult ethical decisions are involved about refusing or withdrawing treatment. Yet these decisions can have a big effect on costs and on the capacity of a unit to accept new, equally complex patients. 'Stark judgemental decisions can … be extremely difficult to make, except perhaps with hindsight' (Ref. 78). But, even with these complicating factors, it does not make sense to respond to pressures, some of which have their origin in areas of the hospital that are cheaper to run, by increasing the number of the most expensive beds.

BOX E

Better planning reduces critical care unit bed pressures

As stated throughout this report, many critical care patients have complex illnesses and there are no 'quick fix' solutions. This box uses simple examples to clarify the effects that a lack of planning can have on bed use. In real life, some of the decisions will be less clear cut. But the principles of explicit, agreed policy and good planning can bring greater consistency and better use of resources in real life, too.

Two different scenarios...	
Lack of planning...	**Trust board involved...**
This general ICU has *six* available beds. All six beds are occupied and a patient needing intensive care must be transferred out because the unit is full:	This general ICU has *four* available beds. Three beds are occupied and the new patient can be admitted to the fourth bed because demand has been better managed:
• beds 1 and 2 are occupied by patients already in need of intensive care on arrival at A&E	• beds 1 and 2 are similarly appropriately occupied
• bed 3 contains an emergency surgical patient who is being ventilated and is at high risk of organ failure	• bed 3 is similarly appropriately occupied
• bed 4 contains a patient who needs intensive care after cardiac arrest; their gradual deterioration and abnormal vital signs had gone undetected on the ward	• training, guidelines and an outreach support system enable detection and prevention of decline into cardiac arrest and the need for this ICU admission is averted
• bed 5 contains a patient with epidural for pain relief after major surgery	• the epidural patient is treated in the surgical ward, where nurses have been specially trained and supported in caring safely for patients with this intervention
• bed 6 contains a patient with chronic bronchitis and associated problems, who was admitted in the night following a sudden decline, but whose death is now considered to be inevitable	• ethical guidelines, agreed at trust level, provide a system for agreeing that it is now in the best interests of this patient to be cared for without intervention outside the ICU
• the unit is unable to respond to a request from another hospital to receive a patient needing intensive care, because it is considered unsafe in the middle of the night to send the epidural patient to the ward	• the request from another hospital for a bed can be accepted because bed 4 is still available
This unit finds itself in an upward spiral of demand and costs. Adding extra beds and staff does not seem to stop demand outpacing supply. Staff feel under stress because they have to transfer patients to other hospitals when the unit is full – for example, during a 'winter crisis'. At other times, the unit is staffed but half-empty.	With trust board involvement, the place of critical care units in the spectrum of care can be planned. The two-way interaction between the critical care units and the rest of the hospital is identified – better care outside units reduces unnecessary pressure on critical care beds, and efficient running of units reduces cancelled operations and critical care costs.
...extra resources are not necessarily meeting needs and improving quality	**...extra resources are better directed to meeting needs**

Note: if a crude measure of efficiency is used – occupancy – the four-bed unit appears less efficient. But looking closer shows that the high occupancy of the six-bed unit occurs because of inappropriate demand. As long as beds are not staffed when empty (Chapter 3), the four-bed unit is the more efficient.

Source: Audit Commission

There can be no simple formula to calculate whether a trust needs, for example, five rather than six beds

Assessing the need for critical care

123. Once the trust is assured that current resources are well used and that inappropriate demand is under control, it can begin to plan for the future. But deciding on bed numbers is complicated by:

- the capacity to transfer patients to and from nearby hospitals;

- how many specialist beds (for example, cardiac, neurosurgery, burns, renal) already exist in the hospital, how well transfer arrangements between them and the general units work (within the limits of specialist staff and equipment capabilities) and whether some integration of specialist and general units could improve efficiency while maintaining clinical expertise;

- variation in professional judgements as to who is or is not an intensive care or high dependency patient, given the openness of the Department of Health guidelines to professional judgement;

- how quickly new techniques and skills training changes the higher-dependency care that wards and other departments can carry out;

- the small size of units – this introduces peaks and troughs of workload that make efficient use of beds difficult, yet any inefficiency has a major impact on costs. In an average size six-bedded unit, one bed occupied unnecessarily represents a 17 per cent waste of resources; and

- the pattern of these peaks and troughs – a unit with predominantly planned admissions of short and predictable lengths of stay might be expected to be able to bear higher occupancy, yet turn away fewer patients than a unit with mainly emergency admissions and unpredictable length of stay. One critical care consultant pointed out that when his unit was nearly full from emergency admissions, it made sense for planned surgery to prioritise patients at least risk of needing subsequent critical care services, where clinical need allowed such choices. But no such planning discussions take place.

124. This means that there can be no simple formula to calculate whether a trust needs, for example, five rather than six beds. Instead, trusts can use the Audit Commission survey tool described in Chapter 3 to find out how well current services are matched to patient needs. How the results translate into bed numbers requires a risk judgement. A balance must be struck between the risk of refusing an admission because the unit is full and the economic benefits of full utilisation of resources. Given that no trust is ever going to be able to fund, and find the staff for, enough beds to cover all the peaks of demand, a decision must be made about how often it is acceptable to transfer patients elsewhere because its own units are all full. One standard recommends that units should be able to admit 95 per cent of all emergencies (Ref. 79). But there is no scientific or moral basis for this figure – each trust must decide for itself what it feels is acceptable, allowing for types of patients and how far they must travel to the next unit.

125. If, after these processes, a trust decides that new beds are needed, the cost of opening them can be daunting. Apart from high equipment costs, some trusts fund the extra nurses needed as a fixed cost, because they staff the bed even if it is unoccupied. But opening a bed will be more affordable if nurses are managed as a variable cost, staffing the bed only when it is occupied and at a nurse:patient ratio that reflects patients' dependency needs. It is also more realistic, given the difficulty that some trusts have in recruiting staff.

Plans

126. Some hospitals experience ward bed-blocking because patients who no longer need acute hospital care have nowhere suitable to be discharged to. This can lead to blockages further up the system – on average, critical care units reported that they retained 2 per cent of patients because there was no free ward bed to send them to. This situation can be avoided by better planning. Some trusts have reconfigured services, making sure that critical care units are seen as integral parts of a network of care, and not as isolated units [CASE STUDY 12].

127. Despite the importance of considering critical care in the context of the whole hospital, few trusts have a written longer-term plan that sets out their development intentions for critical care. This plan should be formulated after wide consultation across the trust. It will then need to be widely advertised so that medical and nursing staff throughout the hospital understand it, not just in critical care units. Once the general plan is made, each unit will need a management policy (Appendix 9).

CASE STUDY 12

Critical care as a planned part of a whole-trust reconfiguration

A trust has redesigned acute services, based on the concept of delivering a seamless service from acute assessment, diagnosis and treatment to rehabilitation. Because 80 per cent of admissions to the critical care area are emergencies, it has been relocated next to A&E and the acute assessment/admissions unit. This reduces patient moves by concentrating services in one area, and focuses the attention of critical care staff on the diagnosis and care planning stages right from the beginning. The growth in critical care beds has been partly funded by the consequently reduced need for medical beds.

Source: Audit Commission site visit

Clinical governance

128. In addition to planning critical care better, trusts also need to introduce clinical governance. One trust chief executive described how the board now requires all departments to present information to the trust board to convince it that they are performing well. The general ICU had recently done so using ICNARC information, and had been the only department so far able to present such comprehensive outcome information.

129. The board must create a framework that assures good performance by making its expectations clear and by fostering a supportive culture within the units [BOX F]. Unit directors acting in isolation may be taking decisions that have a significant impact on trust performance. They need trust-board-agreed guidance as a framework for their daily decision-making. The link between ethics, quality and resources makes critical care a good test-bed of the new clinical governance proposals, which suggest that these are issues that should be debated by clinical staff, managers and non-executives at the trust board. Board-level involvement should lead to lower costs, fewer refused admissions, better quality, a more consistent ethical approach and less stressed staff.

130. Some trust boards will find this a challenge because it is new ground. In addition, it is less easy to agree policy for rare conditions and to make decisions in respect of patients who have several illnesses. These difficulties do not negate the need for the board to debate and agree the ethical framework, but they do make it more difficult to achieve. Central guidance can help in some areas. For example, Department of Health guidelines already specifically state that 'elective ventilation' – subjecting a patient who is expected to die shortly to intervention which is not for the patient's own benefit but for the purposes of organ donation – 'is not permitted' (Ref. 5).

131. Should there also be central guidance about some less easy-to-define areas? For example, can there be central definition of what constitutes 'futile surgery', as described by the most recent National Confidential Enquiry into Perioperative Deaths' (NCEPOD) report? Or should it be left to individual trusts, aided perhaps by scoring systems that can estimate the likely extent of post-operative care needed for a patient? Could central guidance be given about the kind of common occurrence described by an intensive care doctor: 'If you had an 80 year old with an acute cardiac arrest, in the past he would have been allowed to die. Now he is brought into an intensive care unit, treated and sent back to the ward, where he dies two weeks later. Society must decide who we must treat and for how long' (Ref. 81). Or should such broader areas be left to individual trusts to define each for themselves? While it is important to give a degree of autonomy to trusts, discrepancies between local policies in adjoining areas can reinforce a public perception that if treatment is refused it is to save money rather than because it is a clinical judgement about what is ultimately in the best interests of that patient.

The link between ethics, quality and resources makes critical care a good test-bed of the new clinical governance proposals

BOX F

Supporting staff to cope with a stressful environment

Every area of the NHS has its own type of stresses and strains. For critical care staff, the most obvious form of stress is the daily contact with the most near-to-death patients, and with grieving relatives. The reactions to stress can vary, and mutual support among staff is important in coping: 'We just talked and had a good old cry ... I think everyone cried that night. That was absolutely horrible. We were very miserable and we all cried.' But on another occasion in the same unit the way of coping was different: 'We had a good lot of staff on and we laughed a lot that shift, 'cause just when we thought it couldn't get any worse, it did' (Ref. 43).

There has been little research to find out whether there are mechanisms that managers can foster in addition to this kind of informal self-support between staff. It is unknown whether the mechanisms that can support critical care staff in coping with stress are the same or different to the support needed by, for example, the A&E nurse who is at risk of physical or verbal abuse, or the ward nurse who is coping with five or six patients on her own. One study of neonatal critical care nurses found that, in different units, up to one-third of nurses were categorised (by the use of a clinical scale) as anxious, and some felt unsupported at work. The most common things that concerned them organisationally were related to staffing levels, skills shortages, pressures to admit patients when the workload was already high, having responsibility for a new trainee doctor and lack of clear-cut policies [Ref. 80]. Good practice in all of these areas has been described in previous chapters. In addition, it makes sense to:

- arrange a forum for formal discussion at work about stressful events, adding to the informal discussion between staff that usually takes place;
- offer individual counselling services for those who want them;
- improve the induction programmes for new trainee doctors and the higher levels of on-call back up above them, and the training of nurses in the scope of their practice;
- pay attention to the attitudes of senior nurses, doctors and managers – neonatal critical care units where nurses rated these people as supportive and motivating had higher overall nurse well-being scores;
- provide structured orientation and mentoring programmes for new nurses; and
- give nurses the opportunity to discuss their concerns and ways of addressing them as part of a personal development and appraisal system.

Source: Audit Commission, Kite (Ref. 43) and Redshaw et al (Ref. 80)

The country's critical care services

132. This report began by describing variation in how often individual critical care units must transfer patients, or discharge them early, due to pressure on beds. The report then concentrated on helping individual trusts to improve their services. But there are challenges that lie above the level of individual trusts. Anecdotally, some regional groupings of hospitals seem to have to transfer patients more frequently than others. Although it was outside the remit of this study to consider whether the country as a whole has enough, too many or too few critical care beds, the NHS Executive has just completed regional reviews, partly using information provided by the Audit Commission. These reviews are intended to help to plan provision for the coming winter. The NHS Executive and the NHS Directorate for Wales should go on from this to consider whether, in the longer term, explicitly planned 'hub-and-spoke' arrangements, or other forms of configuring specialised services (Ref. 82), could further improve the match between needs and provision.

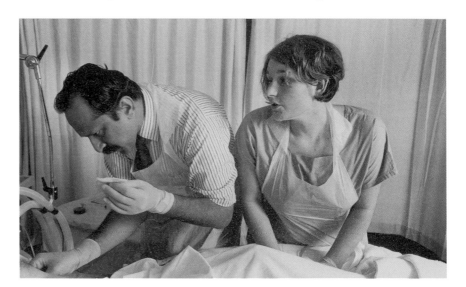

RECOMMENDATIONS

4 Managing a Complex Network

Highest priority recommendations	**Action needed by**
1 Review the degree of board involvement in setting the framework for better use of critical care services.	Chief executive Medical director Non-executive directors
2 Review the configuration of critical care services across the trust; review the extent to which inappropriate demand has been reduced and efficiency improved, before deciding whether increases in the number of critical care unit beds are required.	Chief executive Medical director
3 Agree a critical care management policy that includes the admission and discharge guidelines to units, ethical guidelines, bed management arrangements and who has the power to make within-hospital transfer decisions, targets for the number of refused admissions that the trust is prepared to accept, training plans and audit arrangements.	Medical director
4 Review whether there are gaps in the conditions covered by centrally issued ethical guidance.	NHS Executive NHS Directorate for Wales

Medium priority recommendations	**Action needed by**
5 Agree on the number and type of patients that the trust is prepared to refuse admission to, given the impossibility of funding or recruiting sufficient staff to meet every peak in demand. Ensure transfer arrangements with neighbouring hospitals are in place. Conduct regular outcome audit of patients who are discharged early, are refused admission or transferred.	Chief executive Medical director Non-executive directors
6 Produce a long-term plan for the configuration of critical care services and their inter-relationships with the rest of the hospital. The plan should describe the overall optimum mix of ICU, HDU, general and specialist beds and units. The plan should take account of both demand and supply-side solutions.	Chief executive Medical director Unit leaders

RECOMMENDATIONS

7	Ensure that adequate support arrangements are in place for staff who work in stressful critical care environments – for example, a discussion forum, induction programmes and counselling services.	Chief executive Unit leaders
	Basic recommendations	**Action needed by**
8	Assess how well the need for critical care from within the hospital is being met now, as a starting point for determining the number of critical care unit beds that will be needed in the future.	Chief executive Unit leaders
9	Review the adequacy of critical care provision for populations, including examining current transfer arrangements and whether any future development of 'hub-and-spoke', or other forms of configuring critical care services, is desirable.	NHS Executive NHS Directorate for Wales

Appendix 1

Acknowledgements

The advisory group

Dr Val Chishty	The NHS Executive (Senior Medical Officer)
Peter Clements	Ex-ICU patient (headteacher, retired)
Dr Ruth Endacott	RCN Critical Care Forum (independent nursing adviser)
Sir Terence English	Ex-Audit Commission member (Master, St Catharine's College, Cambridge)
Professor Tim Evans	The Royal College of Physicians (Professor of Intensive Care Medicine, Imperial College School of Medicine; consultant in thoracic and intensive care medicine, Royal Brompton Hospital NHS Trust)
Dr Colin Ferguson	Consultant in anaesthesia and intensive care medicine (The Royal Hospitals NHS Trust and Homerton Hospital NHS Trust)
Dr Paul Lawler	The Intensive Care Society (consultant in anaesthesia and intensive care, South Tees Acute Hospitals NHS Trust)
Wilma McPherson	Director of Quality and Nursing (Guy's and St Thomas' Hospital NHS Trust)
Hugh Ross	Chief Executive (United Bristol Healthcare NHS Trust)
Dr Kathy Rowan	Director (Intensive Care National Audit & Research Centre – ICNARC)
Hilary Rowlands	Audit Commission member (Chief Executive, The Royal Liverpool Children's NHS Trust)
Professor Brian Rowlands	The Royal College of Surgeons (Professor of Surgery, Queen's Medical Centre, University of Nottingham)
Dr David Salter	Senior Medical Officer (Welsh Office)
Dr Carl Waldmann	Director of Intensive Care Unit (Royal Berkshire and Battle Hospitals NHS Trust)
Dr Peter Wallace	The Association of Anaesthetists (Clinical Director of Anaesthesia, Theatres, ITU and Pain Relief Services, West Glasgow Hospitals University NHS Trust)
Dr Sheila Willatts	The Royal College of Anaesthetists (consultant in anaesthesia and intensive care, consultant-in-charge of the ITU, Bristol Royal Infirmary, United Bristol Healthcare NHS Trust)

The interview and data collection sites

We are grateful to the following trusts that assisted with data collection, provided case study information, took part in pilot audits and/or gave of their time for interviews during the study:

Basildon and Thurrock General Hospitals NHS Trust

Central Middlesex NHS Trust

Greenwich Healthcare NHS Trust

Guy's and St Thomas' Hospitals NHS Trust

Huddersfield NHS Trust

James Paget Hospital NHS Trust

Leeds Teaching Hospital NHS Trust

Nottingham City Hospital NHS Trust

Pembrokeshire and Derwen NHS Trust

Plymouth Hospitals NHS Trust

The Princess Alexandra NHS Trust

Royal Berkshire and Battle Hospitals NHS Trust

Royal Bournemouth and Christchurch Hospitals NHS Trust

Royal Surrey County Hospital NHS Trust

South Tees Acute Hospitals NHS Trust

Stockport Acute Services NHS Trust

University College London Hospitals NHS Trust

University Hospital Wales Healthcare NHS Trust

West Middlesex University Hospital NHS Trust

Whiston Hospital, St Helen's and Knowsley NHS Trust

Other sites

We are grateful for informal discussions with many other clinicians and managers within the NHS, and with local auditors.

Appendix 2

Information sources

Study sites

Wide-ranging interviews occurred at six trusts that were chosen to reflect the extremes and average of size and geographical location. In addition, case study visits to interview staff, relatives and ex-patients, or to conduct surveys, took place at other trusts. These are listed in Appendix 1.

National surveys

A postal survey was conducted in 1998. The questionnaire was developed in association with all the major national-level interested parties, and was largely based on one developed previously by ICNARC. It constitutes the most comprehensive survey of critical care services yet carried out in England and Wales. All acute trusts (100 per cent, N = 227 trusts at the time) provided information about the configuration of their services:

- the number of critical care units (both general and specialist) within each trust (and hospital), and beds within them;

- the number of acute beds within each trust; and

- broad management arrangements for critical care.

General ICUs, mixed units and HDUs were asked to complete a more detailed questionnaire. Ninety-four per cent of trusts returned at least one questionnaire, representing 85 per cent (243 units) of the general adult units listed in the trust-wide questionnaires. The questionnaire recorded details about:

- bed types and numbers;

- unit management arrangements;

- relatives' information and accommodation;

- staffing;

- the scope of nursing practice;

- organisation of care;

- deployment systems; and

- patient activity.

A computer package allows local auditors to provide each trust with a data report for their general units showing how they compare with similar units.

All data from the survey are self-reported by trusts. While extreme values have been checked by the Audit Commission with the units concerned, the full verification of data is taking place throughout 1999 as local auditors visit each trust. While it is unknown exactly what, if any, level of inaccuracy is introduced by the use of self-report data, an examination of different methods for calculating occupancy can be given as an example (Ref. 83). This study compared the effect on estimated occupancy of using seven different methods of calculation at a sample of 20 ICUs. Of the seven methods, only one (in use at very few sites, as far as we are aware) produced estimates that differed significantly from those given by the other six. The differences between the other six methods were non-significant and immaterial – for example, a difference between an estimated occupancy of 73.0 per cent and 77.3 per cent. Differences between the most commonly used method (the midnight bedstate) and the most exact method (based on recording the exact times of admission and discharge for each patient) were even smaller – typically less than 1 per cent, and 1.7 per cent for the unit with the biggest difference.

The ways in which beds are used and designated varies between trusts. Beds may physically exist but:

- differ in the level and type of interventions that the bed is equipped to provide (for example, invasive ventilation, haemofiltration);

- funding may not have been identified for the staff needed to open the bed for patients to use; and

- the needed staff may not be in post, or available on the day (for example, because of sickness absence).

No set of definitions will be entirely successful at ensuring that we compare 'like with like'. However, the definitions used in the survey were discussed with previous survey authors and those involved in running critical care services, and take account of the NHS Executive's new Augmented Care Period (ACP) dataset:

- *equipped beds:* the beds exist now and have the necessary equipment to allow them to be used;

- *funded beds:* the budget exists for the nursing and other staff to allow the bed to be used; and

- *available beds:* the staff needed are in post and the bed is generally available to admit patients into.

For most analyses, the number of available beds is used.

ICNARC Case Mix Programme

The Case Mix Programme is a comparative patient outcome audit that is co-ordinated by the Intensive Care National Audit & Research Centre (ICNARC – described further in Appendix 3). Participation is voluntary. Most analyses in this report are based on data for 15,805 admissions to 79 adult intensive care units based in NHS hospitals geographically spread across England, Wales and Northern Ireland. These units are a non-random sample: in some regions all units participate, in others fewer subscribe to the programme. Survival rate figures are from the 52 units that agreed to the use of these data. For more information on the representativeness and quality of these data, please contact ICNARC.

Appendix 3

Adjusting for casemix

Clinicians have established a system of collecting detailed casemix information in which about half of units currently participate (The Intensive Care National Audit & Research Centre - ICNARC). Similar co-operative arrangements exist in some individual English regions and other areas of the UK, allowing participants to compare themselves with other units.

The method used by ICNARC for estimating the expected deaths adjusts for casemix by taking into account how ill the patients are (using the APACHE scoring system) and what is wrong with them. The latter is necessary because, for example, a much higher percentage of patients with gastrointestinal bleeds die than patients with overdoses, even when they have the same APACHE score. Thus the expected hospital mortality for a unit is estimated from a combined knowledge both of how ill each patient is, and their type of illness.

This method is still being developed. Aspects that should be borne in mind when interpreting results include:

- The UK APACHE II model, on which the casemix-adjusted mortality ratios described in Chapter 2 are based, uses data from 1988-90 derived from a smaller number of units than currently participate in the ICNARC programme. The mortality ratios are predominantly above 1.0, the value where the number of observed and expected deaths are equal (that is, at the moment the calculations imply, almost certainly incorrectly, that the majority of units have poorer performance than expected). This is probably due to underestimation of the expected number of deaths. There are several possible reasons for this. The 26 units in the 1988-90 study may not be representative. Alternatively, there may be casemix factors that have not been satisfactorily adjusted for by the model. Or the model may need to be updated for application to 1996-98 data. ICNARC does not consider this to affect the comparative performance of units as depicted in the exhibits. Research begins shortly to optimise the method.

- A unit with significantly different outcome than expected on the basis of one six-month sample could be the result of, for example, an abnormal mix of patients. Only when the survey has been running long enough to identify units with a series of such outcomes in successive sample periods would it be safe to begin to draw conclusions. This effect has been shown by a similar type of audit undertaken in Scottish ICUs. Among 22 units, one in each of three years had significantly higher mortality than expected. However, it was a different unit in each year – no unit had significantly higher than expected mortality for two years in succession (Ref. 84).

- Some ICU doctors help to manage patients in A&E or wards before they are admitted to ICU – this means that the patient's APACHE scores on entering ICU may be lower, because thcy have already been stabilised, but their mortality will reflect the APACHE score when outside the unit. The effect may be to make such unit's outcomes appear less good than a more fairly timed comparison would do (Ref. 85).

Appendix 4

Organisational factors and outcomes

A small number of previous studies have demonstrated links between management, staffing, culture and outcomes within critical care units:

- A study of casemix-adjusted mortality in 26 UK ICUs found that units treating higher numbers of patients did not, overall, have better outcomes than units treating fewer patients – there was no strong evidence for a 'practice makes perfect' effect (Ref. 86).

- A Europe-wide study of 89 units found that lower casemix-adjusted mortality was related to several measures of organisational culture (for example, a higher sense of commitment to the unit and a results-oriented culture) (Ref. 87).

- A study of 42 ICUs in the USA found no significant link between casemix-adjusted mortality and organisational culture. However, technical quality of care was judged to be better, casemix-adjusted lengths of stay were shorter and family needs better met in units where staff perceived there to be effective leadership, good co-ordination with other hospital departments, an ability to resolve conflicts and solve problems and timely, accurate and open communication (Refs. 88 and 89).

- A study of paediatric ICUs in the USA found that the presence of an accredited intensive care specialist was associated with a reduction in casemix-adjusted mortality; size of unit, degree of medical co-ordination, teaching hospital status and trainee doctor cover were not significantly related to mortality differences (Ref. 90).

- A one-hospital study in the USA found that nurse reports of good collaboration between doctors and nurses over the timing of decisions to step patients down to wards were associated with higher casemix-adjusted survival (Ref. 91).

- Another one-hospital study in the USA found improved casemix-adjusted mortality after the introduction of a full-time specialist in critical care medicine (Ref. 92).

- Several single-hospital studies show improved outcomes following a change from an 'open' to 'closed' system (these systems are defined, and the references given, in Chapter 2, 'multidisciplinary communication').

Appendix 5

Patient placement – examples

The purpose of these case descriptions is to open up debate within a trust about whether the most cost-effective policy is being followed. The examples are based on expert opinion, and where some hospitals currently place patients. They are not intended as hard-and-fast rules, but to stimulate debate. Appropriate training and support are needed before a trust changes its current policy.

The descriptions assume that everything else is normal at present (though deterioration with time may occur), and that severity of illness, or potential for critical illness to develop, are recognised. The guidance on suitable locations assumes that a bed is available, and that patients in an HDU are in a position to move to ICU should it become necessary.

Examples of patients placed in an HDU in some hospitals, but in ICU in others

Patient profile	Possible locations
On the cusp of ICU or HDU placement:	
1 66-year-old woman with controlled heart failure and atrial fibrillation after elective abdominoperineal resection.	HDU or ICU – large operation with existing cardiorespiratory disease that may decompensate as a result and needs close monitoring and management.
2 57-year-old woman with pancreatitis; blood glucose 12 mmol/. White blood cell count 17x10^9/L, albumin 30 gm/L	HDU or ICU – blood sugar and white count are up. This is by definition severe acute pancreatitis, which requires full monitoring. Organ failure is likely and support therefore needed.
HDU in some hospitals, but ICU in others:	
3 50-year-old woman with insulin-dependent diabetic mellitus and morbid obesity after abdominal hysterectomy.	HDU – medium surgical trauma but morbid obesity gives risk of respiratory complications that demands active management and close observation. Further complicated by the diabetes, which needs close observation to avoid loss of control.
4 60-year-old woman with four fractured ribs after falling down one flight of stairs. No loss of consciousness.	HDU – risk of respiratory failure due to underlying lung contusion, requires monitoring and support. May go on to require ventilation.
5 42-year-old man admitted with haematemesis of unknown cause and haemoglobin of 6 g/dl, haemodynamically stable with blood transfusion in progress.	HDU – at risk of rebleeding. Needs monitoring and support.

Examples of higher-dependency care that some hospitals carry out on wards, but others on an HDU

Example patient profile or intervention	Possible locations
On the cusp of HDU or ward:	
1 60-year-old man after uncomplicated elective abdominal aortic aneurysm repair.	Specialised ward or HDU - major surgery with no complicating factors. Needs observation to detect post-operative complications.
2 64-year-old chronic bronchitic man on home nebuliser therapy with acute exacerbation. Abnormal blood gases. PH 7.34, $PaCO_2$ 9.0, PaO_2 8 on 28% O_2.	HDU or specialised ward - needs basic respiratory support and close monitoring but not yet advanced respiratory support (ventilation). May be a candidate for non-invasive ventilation.
3 40 per cent or less oxygen via a fixed performance mask. No marked deterioration in respiration over last 24 hours.	The example refers to the stable or improving patient for whom, in isolation and with all else well, care on a general ward should suffice. If the patient has deteriorated since the previous day, then a move to an HDU may be justified. If the patient had been on ICU for two weeks, ventilated, then one week on HDU with mask CPAP, and that improvement was continuing, then a general ward may be appropriate.
4 Mask CPAP or other non-invasive ventilation for acute respiratory failure.	If mask CPAP is used to avoid potential intubation and ventilation in the acute patient, then the patient should be in an HDU. A well-staffed respiratory ward that sees a lot of CPAP may be an appropriate location for patients, but otherwise it is a potentially dangerous procedure that should not be used on a general ward.
5 Vasoactive drugs to support arterial pressure or cardiac output.	It is not uncommon for patients to receive inotrope infusions on a general ward. However, these patients also need blood pressure and heart rate/rhythm monitoring which a general ward may not be able to provide. Alternative placement would then be on an HDU. CCUs and cardiac wards are also appropriate locations.
6 Post-operative epidural analgesic (pain control established).	Some anaesthetists may argue that until pain control is established, patients with epidurals should be in an HDU. Nurses on busy surgical wards may not have time to titrate analgesia effectively. Once controlled however, patients with epidurals should be capable of being cared for on general wards. Many wards do not accept epidurals because of fears of haemodynamic or respiratory complications. Wards may be more willing to accept patients if supported by an acute pain team.

Example patient profile or intervention	Possible locations
Care on the wards in some hospitals, but HDU in others:	
7 ECG monitoring after long operation (patient stable but has significant past cardiac history).	ECG monitoring of a patient is possible on a general ward if (a) staff have enough time to see it and (b) understand what they see. In many hospitals this may not be possible, and patients will be on an HDU. If there is no HDU they may be on an ICU (inefficient use of ICU resources) or on a general ward (but managed poorly).
8 Tracheostomy *in situ*.	A general ward should be able to care for a patient who has a tracheostomy and no other problems. However, many wards either refuse or accept but then manage patients inappropriately.
9 Underwater seal chest drain for resolving a pneumothorax.	Without any complications, such interventions should be possible to manage on a general ward though, as with tracheostomies, this is not always the case. Specialised cardiothoracic wards should definitely be capable of managing these chest drains.
10 A CVP line *in situ* for (a) CVP measurement (patient stable) and crystalloid infusion; (b) total parental nutrition (TPN) infusion.	The presence of a CVP line that is being used for either of these purposes should be the remit of ward staff, but frequently is not.

Source: Audit Commission

Appendix 6

Improving the way that nurse establishments are set

A better way of setting nurse establishments is needed. Among the improvements needed is a more objective, closer relationship to workloads. Although there are methods available that can record objectively how nurses spend some of their time, they are problematic in use. For example, one involves the use of activity recording of the interventions carried out by nurses, which have been assigned standard timings (NEMS – the Nine Equivalents of Nursing Manpower, derived from the TISS system) (Ref. 87). However, the time budget of nurses is related only partly to these activities – nursing workload measures need also to include hygiene and other physical activities, supervising confused or violent un-sedated patients, time spent providing counselling and support for patients and relatives, indirect aspects of care for patients (ordering tests, completing charts and care plans, handover, etc) and other things such as administration, training and management. In fact, NEMS accounts for only 43 per cent of nursing time [TABLE 11]. In addition, to produce a system that can set establishments, it will be necessary to move beyond this to decide how nurses *should* spend their time, given the changing scope of practice and new ways of organising, as discussed in the text.

TABLE 11

How nurses spend their time

	Nurse time	
Implementation of nursing and medical interventions	43%	Activities that form part of the TISS-28 scoring system (for example, maintenance of mechanical ventilation, administration of drugs, basic monitoring [hourly vital signs, regular registration and calculation of fluid balance, etc]). The most time-consuming specific interventions found in this pan-European study were left atrium monitoring (pulmonary artery catheter with or without cardiac output measurement) and peripheral arterial catheter.
Other forms of direct care	13%	For example, psychological support and communication; assisting with activities of daily living (comfort, hygiene, etc).
Subtotal direct care	**56%**	
Indirect care for individual patients	21%	For example, care planning, charting and record keeping, family communications and support, liaising with other disciplines and support services, preparing for admission and discharge, equipment gauging and cleaning.
Subtotal individual patient care	**77%**	
Management, training, etc	3%	For example, meetings, composing the duty rota, stocks, research, training.
Personal time	17%	For example: breaks, toilet, waiting, social interaction with other staff.
Miscellaneous	3%	Anything that does not fit into the above categories.
Subtotal other activities	**23%**	

Source: Miranda et al (Ref. 93)

While waiting for the development of more objective systems, unit managers should use the following, together with the recommendations in Chapter 3, as a checklist against which to assess the way that they currently decide how many nurses to employ **[BOX G, overleaf]**. It is good practice to document the choices made at each step, and to quantify the effect on costs. If costs are higher than in other units, it should be because the unit has taken a conscious decision to adopt higher standards rather than because it is unaware of the cost consequences of its decisions.

BOX G

The steps currently involved in setting a critical care nursing establishment

There are many steps involved in setting a critical care nursing establishment. There are choices that can be made at each of them that will affect staffing costs:

- some units apply a single ratio to all their beds depending on whether the unit is called 'ICU' (a 1:1 ratio for all beds) or 'HDU' (1:2). Other units are more careful to estimate the expected mix of IC and HD patients that will come into their units and weight their calculations accordingly. Some units introduce further levels by acknowledging that some patients may need more than one nurse at certain points during their treatment and some less than a 1:2 ratio. But there are no detailed guidelines on which patients fall into these categories and different units make different judgements;

- whether nurses are replaced when on meal breaks;

- some apply flexibility in interpreting the concepts of 1:1 for ICU patients and 1:2 for HDU – for example, an ICU patient who is still ventilated but has had several medical interventions gradually withdrawn may need less than 1:1 attention, while a high-dependency patient receiving several interventions and who is active and disturbed may need 1:1 attention. Some patients

need more than one nurse at times;

- how the ratio is applied in small HDUs with an odd number of beds can make a substantial difference. When the standard is to have one nurse for every two beds, units with an odd number of beds must either over-staff or fall below the standard. A three-bedded HDU will need two nurses on duty, the same as a four-bedded unit that can potentially treat 25 per cent more patients a year for the same nursing cost;

- whether each shift will have a 'floater' – a nurse (or nurses) in addition to those directly allocated to individual patients. Some units have such nurses, and differ according to whether they are qualified nurses or auxiliaries; other units do not have them at all;

- who has – or has not – been deemed supernumerary in the calculations (for example, the senior nurse, shift leader, 'floater' or 'runner', nurses on induction, nurses on post-basic training);

- the assumptions on which the grade mix has been based (Chapter 3);

- whether the establishment has been calculated on the total number of available beds or on the expected average of occupied beds;

- how the establishment is designed to meet peaks and troughs of work, and the effect of flexible staffing options on nurses needed (for example, flexible shifts, use of overtime to meet peaks, joint establishments between ICU and HDU or other relevant areas, sharing nurses out or standing down to meet troughs);

- the type of shift patterns used – for example, longer shift overlaps, three shifts within the 24-hour period rather than two shifts and high-grade staff working permanent nights – vary the cost of staffing each bed;

- expected absence rates: annual and study leave, short and long-term sickness absence, maternity leave; and

- expected turnover, and whether these posts will be covered from the funded establishment while vacant.

Source: Audit Commission

Appendix 7

Assessing the need for critical care

The Audit Commission has developed a decision flow-chart that can be used to assess an individual patient's need for different levels of care. It can be used to assess patients across the hospital and therefore provide an estimate of the number of patients with a need for intensive, high-dependency and ward care. Carried out over a sufficient period of time, and in association with improved efficiency and off-unit care as described in Chapter 3, it can form the basis of a trust's plans for configuring its services and bed numbers. Copies of the flow-chart are available via local appointed auditors.

The tool is based on the Department of Health criteria for admission to intensive care and high dependency units, and on a form developed by Ninewells Hospital, Dundee, but requires a clearer, more explicit choice to be made between the ICU, HDU and ward as the appropriate location. To make professional judgements more objective, the Audit Commission tool requires the type of observation/monitoring needed to be recorded. As a result, the trust will be able to quantify the effect of policy changes on bed requirements. For example, if current policy is to nurse epidural patients on an HDU, the survey will record how many beds are used in this way and enable an estimate of the reduced demand for HDU beds if ward staff are trained and supported to provide this care there instead.

Appendix 8

Checklist for evaluating tools that assess the need for critical care

Some trusts have carried out their own surveys to assess the need for critical care. They vary in design quality. This checklist can be used to evaluate the quality of such surveys.

Sponsorship

1 The survey is overseen by a trust-wide steering committee including the medical director, intensive care doctors, physicians, surgeons, nurses (critical care and ward) and managers.

2 There is commitment in the trust to the survey and a plan of how the results will be taken forward (including further work that will be needed to interpret the results and develop solutions).

3 The survey is carried out, and results analysed and interpreted, by a range of people, and not just critical care unit staff or others who might have a vested interest in the outcome.

Objectives

4 Objectives are clearly stated and impartial, and do not anticipate the findings, conclusions or remedial action needed.

Scope

5 Includes patients in high-dependency and intensive care units, general wards and extended period recovery areas and admissions wards.

Period and timing

6 Period, timing and coverage of survey are such that results are representative of normal activity.

Assessment process

7 There is a timetable for assessments and a record that assessments have been carried out.

8 Weekends and bank holidays are included in the survey.

9 Assessments are made at the bedside and are based on a combination of observation, review of patients' notes and discussion with ward sisters.

10 There is a protocol on how the assessment process works.

11 Assessments are subject to reliability checks by others.

12 Assessments are subject to reliability checks by staff who are not assessors (for example, by members of the steering committee, or medical staff who work on wards).

13 There is a process to resolve disagreements (for example, a third assessment).

Assessments

14 There are pre-printed forms for recording results of assessments.

15 There is an 'audit trail' that shows the reasons and measurements that support the assessment.

16 Assessments only take into account patients' actual needs. They do not anticipate 'hidden' demands that might emerge if resources were available to meet them.

Assessors

17 Assessors are independent of the areas under review (if this is impossible, greater emphasis needs to be placed on the reliability checks).

18 Assessors (and staff doing reliability checks) have instruction/training in how to assess patients.

Appendix 9

Critical care management policy

Chapter 4 recommends that each trust should develop a critical care management policy. This appendix provides a checklist of basic contents. The policy will need to be drawn up after trust-wide discussion and should include:

- criteria for admission to, and discharge from, each critical care unit (that is, specifying the type of patients that are appropriate for the unit);

- guidelines on where patients with terminal or persistent but unrecoverable illness should be treated;

- the physiological (and other) triggers that ward staff should use to seek admittance to units, or advice from critical care staff about management;

- details of arrangements for bed management within and between each unit, including who has the power to make decisions;

- criteria for transferring a patient out of the hospital to another hospital, both for specialist treatment and because there are no free beds within the hospital's own units;

- details of how transfers should be arranged and carried out;

- policy for determining the staffing requirements of different patients in the unit, according to their dependency needs;

- details of how to book an elective case; an agreed policy to follow if elective admissions have to be cancelled;

- targets for the number of such cancellations;

- details of how discharges are to be arranged and patients and relatives prepared;

- the training arrangements designed to deliver the policy; and

- audit arrangements to check for compliance with each of the above arrangements.

Source: Audit Commission

Glossary

ACP data set	The NHS Executive's Augmented Care Period data set. An 'augmented care period' is defined as the total number of days that the patient received intensive care and/or high-dependency care. Every admission to a unit is included. The NHS Directorate for Wales has not yet required the ACP to be mandatory.
APACHE	Acute Physiology and Chronic Health Evaluation. The APACHE II score gives an indication of the severity of a patient's illness.
BACCN	British Association of Critical Care Nurses.
Blood gas analysis	Measurement of a blood sample (usually arterial blood) to determine the acidity of the blood, and how much oxygen and carbon dioxide is in it.
Cardiac arrest	Sudden cessation of cardiac output and effective circulation. Immediate resuscitation is required to prevent heart, lung, kidney and brain damage.
CCU	Coronary or cardiac care unit.
Chest drain	A catheter inserted into the chest cavity for the removal of air or fluid.
Clinician	A health professional directly involved in the care and treatment of patients (for example, doctors, nurses, therapists).
CPAP	Continuous positive airway pressure. A breathing support system where the patient breathes in and out from a pressurised gas source. The high pressure helps to distend the lungs and eases the breathing.
Critical Care Nursing Forum	Membership of this Royal College of Nursing Forum is for any nurse engaged in the care of the critically ill. The Forum addresses all professional issues related to critical care nursing and brings these to the attention of appropriate bodies.
CVP line	Central venous pressure line. A narrow catheter that is inserted into a vein in the neck or arm. It is threaded onwards towards the heart where it is used to monitor the heart's functions.
ENB, WNB	English National Board, Welsh National Board. These organisations provide a framework for continuing education for nurses and specific courses enabling nurses to gain specialist qualifications.
Epidural analgesia	The process of achieving regional analgesia of the pelvic, abdominal, genital or other area by the injection of drugs into the epidural space of the spinal column.
Extubation	The process of withdrawing a tube from a patient's airway.
HCA	Health care assistant. A person who has normally trained under the NVQ system (see below).
HDU	High dependency unit.
ICNARC	Intensive Care National Audit & Research Centre. ICNARC was established following the results of the UK APACHE II study (see above). It audits and researches intensive care practices and outcomes. One of its

activities is to collect very detailed data on IC patients from its members (ICUs in the UK) and feed back data on predicted outcomes.

ICS   Intensive Care Society   The ICS was founded in 1970 and was the first society in the world to bring together clinicians whose main interest was caring for critically ill patients. The Society has multi-specialty membership and includes physicians, surgeons, clinical physiologists and pathologists, although the majority (over 80 per cent) of members are anaesthetists.It promotes education and research in intensive care medicine by publishing standards and recommendations.

ICU   Intensive care unit.

Inotropes   Drugs that make the heart muscle work harder, for example, adrenalin.

Intercollegiate Board for Training in Intensive Care Medicine   The Intercollegiate Committee for Training in Intensive Care Medicine had its first meeting in March 1993. It comprised representatives from the Royal Colleges of Anaesthetists, Physicians and Surgeons and the Intensive Care Society. The Committee's remit was to establish a training pattern for doctors who wish to practice intensive care, and to approve hospitals suitable to provide that training. It became the Intercollegiate Board in 1997.

Intubation   The insertion of a tube through the mouth or nose, or into the trachea, to ensure that a patient's airway is clear for the delivery of gaseous drugs and oxygen.

ITU   Intensive therapy unit – an alternative description of an ICU.

IV   Intravenous.

National Intensive Care Bed Register   The Register currently comprises four local services, listing available intensive care beds in all general adult, paediatric and neurosciences ICUs in England. Units are contacted several times a day and information about available beds and services is recorded. It is accessible 24 hours a day and it directs clinicians who are trying to locate intensive care beds for specific patients towards appropriate units with the capacity to help.

NCCG   Non consultant career grade doctor. NCCG doctors include: trust grades, staff grades, clinical assistants and associate specialists.

NCEPOD   The National Confidential Enquiry into Perioperative Deaths.

NVQ   National Vocational Qualification. Government scheme of mainly on-the-job training with participants required to attain various competencies determined by their (in-house) assessors. The normal initial qualification is level 2, some trusts are now training to level 3 and 4.

TISS   Therapeutic Intervention Scoring System. A TISS score for a patient gives an indication of nursing workload. It measures the amount of nursing intervention that a patient needs.

TPN   Total parenteral nutrition means that nutrition is provided to the patient intravenously.

Tracheostomy   Tracheostomy is the surgical insertion of a tube into the trachea, allowing prolonged mechanical ventilation.

References

1. Audit Commission, *Lying in wait: The Use of Medical Beds in Acute Hospitals*, Audit Commission/HMSO, London, 1992.

2. Association of Anaesthetists, *Intensive Care Services: Provision for the Future*, AAGBI, London, 1988.

3. Metcalfe A & McPherson K, *Study of the Provision of Intensive Care in England, 1993: Revised Report for the Department of Health*, London School of Hygiene & Tropical Medicine, London, 1995.

4. Ridley S, Burchett K, Gunning K, Burns A, Kong A, Wright M, Hunt P & Ross S, 'Heterogeneity in Intensive Care Units: Fact or Fiction?', *Anaesthesia*, vol. 52, 1997, pp531-7.

5. Department of Health, *Guidelines on Admission to and Discharge from Intensive Care and High Dependency Units*, NHS Executive, Leeds, 1996.

6. Intensive Care Society, *Standards for Intensive Care Units*, Intensive Care Society, London, 1997.

7. Lassen H C A, 'A Preliminary Report on the 1952 Epidemic of Poliomyelitis in Copenhagen with Special Reference to the Treatment of Acute Respiratory Insufficiency', *The Lancet*, Jan.3, 1953, pp37-41.

8. Audit Commission, *Pain after Surgery: results of National Survey*, Audit Commission, London, 1998.

9. Ball J & Stock J, *Nurses and technicians in high technology areas*, IMS report no.239, Brighton, 1992.

10. Edbrooke D, Hibbert C, Ridely S, Long T, Dickie H et al., 'The Development of a Method of Comparative Costing of Individual Intensive Care Units', *Anaesthesia*, vol. 54, 1999, pp110-120.

11. Royal College of Anaesthetists and Royal College of Surgeons, *Report of the Joint Working Party on Graduated Patient Care*, RCA/RCS, London, 1996.

12. Edbrooke D, Talk Cited in Intensive Care Society Newsletter, Spring 1998.

13. Griffiths R D, 'Development of Normal Indices of Recovery from Critical Illness', Intensive Care Yearbook, Intensive Care Society, 1993.

14. Cochrane Injuries Group Albumin Reviewers, 'Human Albumin Administration in Critically Ill Patients: Systematic Review of Randomised Controlled Trials', *British Medical Journal*, vol. 317. 1998, pp235-40.

15. Lawler P G & Morgan G A, 'Modified Editorial might have Restrained Media Response', *British Medical Journal*, vol. 317, 1998, p885.

16. Shelly M P, 'Sedation in the ICU', *Care of the Critically Ill*, vol. 14, 1998, pp85-8.

17. Rowan K M, *Outcome Comparisons of Intensive Care Units in Great Britain and Ireland using the APACHE II Method*, DPhil thesis, University of Oxford, 1992.

18. King's Fund, 'Intensive Care in the United Kingdom: Report from the King's Fund Panel', *Anaesthesia*, vol. 44, 1989, pp428-31.

19. Parmar M & Criswell J, 'Evidence Based Medicine', *Care of the Critically Ill*, vol. 14, 1998, p218.

20. MacKirdy F N & Howie J C, 'The Value of the Pulmonary Artery Catheter', *British Journal of Intensive Care*, vol. 9, 1999, p98.

21. Waldmann C & Gaine M, 'The Intensive Care Follow-up Clinic', *Care of the Critically Ill*, vol. 12, 1996, pp118-121.

22. Rosenthal H, 'An Alien Place', *Nursing Times*, vol. 92, 1996, pp48-9.

23. Intensive Care Society, *Guidelines for Bereavement Care in ICUs*, Intensive Care Society, London, 1998.

24. Paediatric Intensive Care Society, *Standards for Paediatric Intensive Care, Including Standards of Practice for Transportation of the Critically Ill Child*, Saldatore, Bishops Stortford, 1996.

25. Jones C, Hussey R & Griffiths R D, 'A Tool to Measure the Change in Health Status of Selected Adult Patients Before and After Intensive Care', *Clinical Intensive Care*, vol. 4, 1993, pp160-5.

26. Ridley S A & Wallace P G M, 'Quality of Life After Intensive Care', *Anaesthesia*, vol. 45, 1990, pp808-13.

27. Ridley S A, Chrispin P S, Scotton H, Rogers J and Lloyd D, 'Changes in Quality of Life After Intensive Care: Comparison with Normal Data', *Anaesthesia*, vol. 52, 1997, pp195-202.

28. Jones C, MacMillan R R, Harris C & Griffiths R D, 'Severe Tracheal Stenosis Associated with Reintubation', *Clinical Intensive Care*, vol. 8, 1997, pp122-5.

29. Sharland C, Huggett A & Nielsen M, 'Persistent Pruritis After Hydroxyethyl Starch (HES) Infusions in Critically Ill Patients', *Critical Care*, vol. 3, 1999, p75.

30. Jones C, MacMillan R R & Griffiths R D, 'Providing Psychological Support for Patients After Critical Illness', *Clinical Intensive Care*, vol. 5, 1994, pp176-9.

31. Jones C, *Intensive Care Recovery Manual*, Whiston Hospital, 1998.

32. Irvine D, 'The Performance of Doctors. I. Professionalism and Self Regulation in a Changing World. II. Maintaining Good Practice, Protecting Patients from Poor Performance', *British Medical Journal*, vol. 314, 1997, pp1540-2 and pp1613-5.

33. Euricus, *Field Research Manual Two*, Groningen, 1998.

34. Ghorra S, Reinert S E, Cioffi W, Buczko G & Simms H H, 'Analysis of the Effect of Conversion from Open to Closed Surgical Intensive Care Unit', *Annals of Surgery*, vol. 229, 1999, pp163-171.

35. Hanson C W, Deutschman C S, Anderson H L, Reilly P M, Behringer E C, Schwab C W & Price J, 'Effects of an Organized Critical Care Service on Outcomes and Resource Utilization: a Cohort Study', *Critical Care Medicine*, vol. 27, 1999, pp270-4.

36. Carson S S, Stocking C, Podsadecki T, Christenson J, Pohlman A, MacRae S, Jordan J, Humphrey H, Siegler M & Hall J, 'Effects of Organizational Change in the Medical Intensive Care Unit of a Teaching Hospital: a Comparison of 'Open' and 'Closed' Formats', *Journal of the American Medical Association*, vol. 276, 1996, pp322-8.

37. Foley P T, Baldock G J & Brett S J, *Impact of Changes in Staffing and Organisation of an Intensive Care Unit on Outcome*, Paper Presented at European Intensive Care Association, 1999.

38. Intensive care consultant, pers. comm.

39. Audit Commission, *The Virtue of Patients: Making Best Use of Ward Nursing Resources*, Audit Commission/HMSO, 1993.

40. Institute of Medicine Guidelines for Clinical Practice, cited in Barker R & Fraser R C, 'Development of Review Criteria: Linking Guidelines and Assessment of Quality', *British Medical Journal*, vol. 311, 1995, pp370-3.

41. Royal College of Nursing Critical Care Forum, *The Nature of Nursing Work in Intensive Care*, RCN, London, 1997.

42. Greenhalgh and Company Ltd, *The Interface Between Junior Doctors and Nurses: a Research Study for the Department of Health*, DoH, 1994.

43. Kite K, *Learning to Doubt: the Professional Development of Nurses in One Intensive Therapy Unit*, PhD thesis, University of East Anglia, 1998.

44. Fogarty M, 'Let assistants take the strain', *Healthcare Management*, April 1993, pp54-6.

45. Kollef M H et al., 'A Randomised Control Trial of Protocol-Directed Versus physician Directed Weaning from Mechanical Ventilation', *Critical Care Medicine*, vol. 25, 1997, pp567-74.

46. Song R, Daly B J, Rudy E B, Douglas S and Dyer M A, 'Nurses' Job Satisfaction, Absenteeism and Turnover after Implementing a Special Care Unit Practice Model', *Research in Nursing and Health*, vol. 20, 1997, pp443-52.

47. Atkinson S, Bihari D, Smithies M, Daly K, Mason R and McColl I, 'Identification of Futility in Intensive Care', *The Lancet*, vol. 344, 1994, pp1203-1206.

48. National Confidential Enquiry into Perioperative Deaths, 1996/97 report, NCEPOD, London, 1998.

81.   The Times, January 1999.

82.   Audit Commission, *Higher Purchase: Commissioning Specialised Services in the NHS*, Audit Commission, 1997.

83.. Ridley S & Rowan K, 'Be Wary of Occupancy Figures', *Health Trends*, vol. 29, 1998, pp100-105.

84.   Scottish Intensive Care Society Audit Group, *An Audit of Intensive Care Units in Scotland, Annual Report 1998*, Scottish Intensive Care Society, 1999.

85.   Tunnell R D, Millar B W & Smith G B, 'The Effect of Lead Time Bias on Severity of Illness Scoring, Mortality Prediction and Standardised Mortality Ratio in Intensive Care – a PILOT study', *Anaesthesia*, vol. 53, 1998, pp1045-53.

86.   Jones J & Rowan K, 'Is there a relationship between the volume of work carried out in intensive care and its outcome?,' *International Journal of Technology Assessment in Health Care*, vol. 11, 1995, pp762-9.

87.   Reis Miranda D, Ryan D W, Schaufeli W B & Fidler V (eds), *Organisation and Management of Intensive Care: a Prospective Study in 12 European Countries*, Springer, Berlin, 1998.

88.   Shortell S M, Zimmerman J E, Gillies R R, Duffy J, Devers K J, Rousseau D M & Knaus W A, 'Continuously Improving Patient Care: Practical Lessons and an Assessment Tool from the National ICU study', *QRB*, May 1992, pp50-155.

89.   Shortell S M, Zimmerman J E, Rousseau D M, Gillies R R, Wagner D P, Draper E A, Knaus W A & Duffy J, 'The Performance of Intensive Care Units: Does Good Management Make a Difference?', *Medical Care*, vol. 32, 1994, pp508-25.

90.   Pollack M M, Cuerdon T T, Patel K M, Ruttimann U E, Getson P R & Levetown M, 'Impact of Quality of Care Factors on Pediatric Intensive Care Mortality', *Journal of the American Medical Association*, vol. 272. 1994, pp941-6.

91.   Baggs J G, Ryan S A, Phelps C E, Richeson J F & Johnson J E, 'The Association Between Interdisciplinary Collaboration and Patient Outcomes in a Medical Intensive Care Unit', *Heart & Lung*, vol. 21, 1992, pp18-24.

92.   Brown J J & Sullivan G, 'Effect on ICU Mortality of a Full-Time Critical Care Specialist', *Chest*, vol. 96, 1989, pp127-9.

93.   Reis Miranda D, de Rijk A & Schaufeli W, 'Simplified Therapeutic Intervention Scoring System: The TISS-28 Items – Results From a Multicenter Study', *Critical Care Medicine*, vol. 24, 1996, pp64-73.

Index
References are to paragraph numbers, appendices, boxes and case studies.

1  Reviewing the Service

2  Improving Survival and Quality of Life

3 Reducing Costs through Flexibility

4 Managing a Complex Network

Contents

© Audit Commission 1999

First published in October 1999 by the Audit Commission for Local Authorities and the National Health Service in England and Wales, 1 Vincent Square, London SW1P 2PN

Typeset by Ministry of Design, Bath

Printed in the UK for the Audit Commission by Holbrooks Printers, Portsmouth

ISBN 1 86240 187 X

Photographs: David Mansell